Connect to NCTM Standards 2000

Making the Standards Work at Grade 6

Francis (Skip) Fennell, Ph.D.
Honi J. Bamberger, Ph.D.
Thomas E. Rowan, Ph.D.
Kay B. Sammons
Anna R. Suarez

Creative Publications®
A Tribune Education Company

Acknowledgments

Project Editors → Diane Nieker, Jeff Stiegel

Writers → Tim Burnett, Marilyn Davis, Beth Sycamore

Writing and Editorial Services → MathLink, Inc.

Design Director → Karen Stack

Design → Gerta Sorensen-London

Project Coordinator → Barbara Quincer

Cover Illustration → Jim Dandy

Illustrators → Susan Aiello, Jim Dandy, Sarah Frederking

Production → Inkwell Publishing Solutions, Inc.

Manufacturing → Dallas Richards

Two Prudential Plaza
Chicago, IL 60601

This is an independent publication and is not affiliated with, or sponsored by, the NCTM. The NCTM 2000 Standards are not reproduced in this book. This book is designed to be read independently of the *Principles and Standards for School Mathematics* and to aid educators in preparing to teach in a manner consistent with the *Principles and Standards*.

ISBN 0-7622-1248-9
Catalog No. 21608
Customer Service 800-624-0822
http://www.creativepublications.com
1 2 3 4 5 6 7 8 MAL 05 04 03 02 01 00

Contents

Overview

Since *Curriculum and Evaluation Standards for School Mathematics* was released in 1989, much has been learned about how ideas work in the classroom and how students learn mathematics. The release of the *Principles and Standards for School Mathmatics* creates an opportunity for us to examine our goals, our math curricula, and our teaching methods in light of these new insights and to consider practices and procedures that will improve school mathematics education. As did the original draft, *Principles and Standards* promotes ways for all educators to strengthen the teaching and learning of mathematics by addressing two important concerns: the characteristics of instructional programs that will provide high-quality mathematical experiences for students as they progress through school, and the mathematical content and processes students should know and use as they advance from grade to grade.

Content Standards

Number and Operation

Algebra

Geometry

Measurement

Data Analysis and Probability

Process Standards

Problem Solving

Reasoning and Proof

Communication

Connections

Representation

General Overview

Connect to NCTM Standards 2000 is designed to help you understand and implement the NCTM standards. Regardless of your teaching style, the information presented in this book will help you to make the standards work. *Principles and Standards* identifies ten standards. Five of those standards are described as content standards that organize all of mathematics into five broad areas of learning; they address *what* students learn. The other five standards, the process standards, are concerned with *how* students learn and how information is presented.

Today, more than ever, there is a need for all students to have a strong base in mathematics. This means that students do not just memorize facts and procedures, but that they have an understanding of mathematics and mathematical thinking. The interplay between content and process is complicated, but integrating the two is critical if our students are to receive the mathematics education they will need to function effectively in the world they will grow into.

The lessons contained within *Connect to NCTM Standards 2000* are organized into sections by content. Each section contains four lessons dealing with some aspect of that content standard. Each lesson demonstrates ways to develop the content by using the process standards. An overview highlights grade-level content skills and gives a brief description of the four lessons for that standard.

The last section of the book, entitled Create Your Own, is designed to help you develop lessons of your own that will comfortably incorporate the NCTM standards with your teaching style.

About the Lessons

Each content standard section contains four lessons that address some aspect of the content at the grade level. Three of the lessons have been specially developed to model ways the process standards can be used to develop the content being presented. The fourth lesson examines a typical math textbook lesson in terms of how the process standards are incorporated into that lesson. Suggestions are offered for increasing the focus on three of the five process standards to create a more effective lesson. Then a lesson is presented modeling how those suggestions can be implemented.

As you read through the lessons, keep in mind that what is offered is only one possible approach. You might have a completely different idea about how to develop the concept, and that's fine. These lessons are intended to provide examples of how the process standards can work to make mathematics lessons more meaningful, and, to model questions and techniques that you might incorporate into your teaching. As you read through the lessons, pay attention to how the process standards are being used. Use the ideas presented as a springboard for your own ideas.

Each lesson is intended for a single class period. Some introduce a concept, others require students have some experience with the concept, and still others are meant to be used at the end of a unit. As you examine these lessons, think about how and where they fit into your curriculum. Any of the lessons here can be used as a replacement for the comparable lesson in your current math program. Try the lessons and see the difference incorporating the process standards can make.

Creating Your Own Lessons

The last section of the book is designed to help you develop lessons of your own that incorporate the NCTM standards and are compatible with your teaching style. You will find questions to help you focus on ideas to consider as you begin to organize a standards-based lesson. You will also have an opportunity to follow the thoughts and decisions one person used in the process of developing a lesson.

About the Authors

Francis (Skip) Fennell, Ph.D.

Dr. Fennell was a member of the writing team of *Principles and Standards for School Mathematics* (NCTM, 2000). He has authored mathematics textbooks, materials for both students and teachers, and numerous articles for leading mathematics journals. Dr. Fennell has served on the Board of Directors of NCTM and as Program Officer of instructional materials and teacher enhancement within the Division of Elementary, Secondary, and Informal Education at the National Science Foundation. He has been selected as Outstanding Mathematics Educator by the Maryland Council of Teachers of Mathematics, and as Professor of the Year by both the Carnegie Foundation and Western Maryland College, where he is a professor of education.

Honi J. Bamberger, Ph.D.

Dr. Bamberger is a recognized math scholar and teacher. She has taught at both the elementary school and college levels, served as an associate research scientist and mathematics consultant for Johns Hopkins University, and contributed as a consultant and content writer for the "Numbers Alive" public television series. Dr. Bamberger has presented her research findings at mathematics conferences across the country, and has been an author for a number of mathematics textbooks. Currently, Dr. Bamberger is executive director of Insight, a consulting firm specializing in professional development in mathematics education.

Thomas E. Rowan, Ph.D.

Dr. Rowan was a member of the working group that wrote the K–4 section of the *Curriculum and Evaluation Standards for School Mathematics.* Since the Standards were first published, he has worked with many school systems to help bring about the transition to standards-based classroom mathematics instruction in grades K–8. Dr. Rowan is a frequent presenter at NCTM and author of mathematics texts and numerous articles on teaching and learning mathematics. He currently teaches at the University of Maryland where he focuses on methods of teaching elementary school mathematics.

Kay B. Sammons

Kay Sammons is currently Elementary Mathematics Supervisor for the Howard County Public Schools in Ellicott City, Maryland, where she is responsible for curriculum and staff development for elementary teachers. She is a frequent presenter at state and national mathematics conferences. In addition to serving as a reviewer for NCTM publications, she has written textbooks and teacher resource materials. Ms. Sammons was honored as Elementary Mathematics Teacher of the Year by the Maryland Council Teachers of Mathematics and as Outstanding Educator of the Year by that same organization.

Anna R. Suarez

Anna Suarez is a national consultant and program director for K–8 Mathematics at the National Science Foundation in Arlington, Virginia. Her participation in an NSF-funded research study, Cognitively Guided Instruction (C.G.I.), helped to develop teachers' knowledge of students' mathematical thinking as the basis for making instructional decisions. She has written staff development materials for both the *Investigations* curriculum and Insight.

About the Standards

The *Principles and Standards for School Mathematics* are built around ten curriculum standards. Five of those standards address the mathematical content, or body of mathematical knowledge, that students should learn. These content standards prescribe *what* is to be taught in mathematics. The content standards are Number and Operation, Algebra, Geometry, Measurement, and Data Analysis and Prbability.

The other five standards are process standards. The process standards describe *how* the content is delivered. They address how students will acquire the necessary mathematical content and how that knowledge will be applied. The five process standards are identified as Problem Solving, Reasoning and Proof, Communication, Connections, and Representation.

It should be pointed out that the content standards and process standards are not separate subsets of the whole, but are intricately interrelated. How mathematics is learned is as important as what mathematics is learned. The process standards help to "frame" how the content standards are presented.

It is possible to weave the process standards into the teaching of mathematics through a variety of methods. Students can and should be presented with meaningful problems to solve and situations that require them to reason through information to find solutions. They should be asked to defend their solutions and explain their thinking. In presenting a problem to students, connections might be made to a similar problem to build on previous learning. A representative model might be used to enhance students' understanding of a concept. Continuous communication, written and oral, will provide feedback about students' understanding.

For students to become mathematically powerful, it is essential that they be able to use process skills flexibly. They need to practice applying reasoning to solve problems and proving that their solutions are correct. They need to experiment with a variety of representations and have the ability to use them in solving problems and in illustrating their thinking. They should be able to communicate their mathematical thinking and solutions to the teacher and to other students both orally or in writing. Making connections between problems within mathematics is as essential as is making mathematical connections to disciplines outside of mathematics. The importance of how these processes interrelate and work together cannot be overemphasized.

Content Standards

Number and Operation

Algebra

Geometry

Measurement

Data Analysis and Probability

Process Standards

Problem Solving

Reasoning and Proof

Communication

Connections

Representation

Middle School Problem Solving

PROBLEM SOLVING IS AT THE HEART of mathematics—it is what mathematicians do. Balance is achieved through the interrelationship of conceptual learning, basic skills, and problem solving. Students need to develop concepts with concrete representations to ensure understanding and to build a strong foundation. They need basic skills in order to apply their understandings with efficiency. But most importantly, they need good problems to solve, problems in which they can utilize their conceptual understanding and basic skills.

In its simplest form, problem solving means finding a solution when the answer is not readily apparent. Because problem solving does not always follow a uniform plan, students need to develop persistence to be able to work problems through to the end. Sometimes persistence means changing direction. *Well, we know that way doesn't work. What should we try next? Is there another way we can look at this problem?* Questions that encourage students to look for other options should be an integral part of the discussions that take place in mathematics classes.

Choosing problems that have relevance to students is an important factor in creating enthusiasm for problem solving. Often, the enthusiasm of the teacher translates into a positive disposition toward problem solving for students. If statements like, *Now that's an unusual problem. I wonder how we can find the answer,* are part of a teacher's repertoire, students get the notion that problem solving is pretty interesting stuff and they are encouraged to use their own resources to find a path to the solution.

Acquiring a variety of strategies to access for problem solving is essential to experiencing success. Having flexibility to solve problems in different ways enables students to get "unstuck" if they reach a "dead end." Students should be provided with instruction and practice in using a wide range of strategies that they can then draw upon.

When students are presented with a problem that doesn't exactly fit into the context of what they already know, they need to know how to develop strategies based on their previously learned skills and concepts.

This problem was presented to a class of seventh grade students.

> **The recipe for the punch that we are serving at the dance on Friday makes 8 gallons. A punch glass holds $\frac{3}{4}$ cup of punch. Will 8 gallons be enough to serve all 75 of the students expected to attend the dance? If not, how much more punch will be needed? Work with your group and show your work on paper. Be prepared to present your solution to the class.**

This is a real-world problem that is relevant to students. The wonderful thing is that like most real mathematics problems encountered outside of the classroom, it's a messy problem.

First, students need some information they're not given. Will some students want more than one serving punch? How many students will decline the punch? How many servings at $\frac{3}{4}$ cup each are there in 8 gallons? Second, students will need to decide how and where they can get the information they need. Third, since there is really no precise answer to a problem like this, students will need to use their estimation and reasoning skills.

Each group might approach this problem a little differently. Some will immediately pick up a calculator and start figuring; others might start with a visual representation. In the process of solving the problem, students might approach the head of the dance committee to see how many tickets have been

sold, or they might canvass their friends as to their preference for punch. They might consult a standards measure table to find equivalent measures for cups, pints, quarts, and gallons.

When the task has been completed, each group should have an opportunity to present and defends its solution. A wide range of approaches and solutions will emerge. These different strategies should be compared noting similarities and differences. Students should also be asked to consider which solutions they think work best for the particular problem and why. This opens the door to a rich discussion that will broaden the learning experience for all.

Problem solving is at the core of any mathematics curriculum; it is integral to all mathematical activity. As such, it should permeate the entire mathematics program. Students who are consistently presented with challenging problems learn to develop and apply new strategies. When they are also given opportunities to communicate their strategies with others and reflect on their thinking, their problem solving abilities are further enhanced.

Middle School Reasoning and Proof

REASONING IS FUNDAMENTAL TO THE STUDY of mathematics—it is a state of mind that causes students to explore, to justify, and to validate. It permeates all content areas and all grade levels. Students are reasoning when they interpret data, when they solve problems, and when they view geometric patterns and shapes. As they are presented with new problems, they use reasoning skills to apply previously acquired information and to test the validity of their solutions. Reasoning is the process by which students make sense of mathematics.

As they develop mathematically, students learn that mathematics is a discipline based on an inherent set of rules. Reasoning begins with intuition. This intuition is used by even the youngest children in their efforts to make sense of mathematics, and it should be encouraged as the basis of reasoning at all grade levels. This informal intuition will become the basis for reasoning through representations that are more formal and for proofs based upon the rules.

What are some ways reasoning and proof can be incorporated into the mathematics class? An excellent way is to ask questions that hold students accountable for their thinking. *How did you get your answer? Tell me how you thought about that. Why does your solution work? Do you think that strategy will always work?*

Piaget believed that for students to develop reasoning, it was imperative to have social interaction. A powerful means of achieving this interaction is through mathematical discussions. Designating time during the class for students to put forth their ideas for examination is critical. Students must learn to explain and defend their thinking. They must also learn to detect unsound reasoning in explanations presented by other students. In any given class there will be a wide range of reasoning abilities and it is helpful for students with less mature reasoning to hear from those with well-developed skills. These mathematical discussions increase a student's repertoire of reasoning skills.

What do these mathematical discussions look like? A teacher typically presents a problem to the class that may be related to concepts being studied. A class of sixth grade students working on figuring percentages was presented with the following problem:

What is 75% of 80?

After allowing a few minutes for students to work independently to figure out the solution, the teacher, Mr. Matthews, invited the students to share their solutions and strategies with another classmate.

"How many of you got the same answer as the person you shared with?" Most hands were raised.

"How many of you used the exact same strategy as that person?" Fewer than half the students responded.

"O.K. Let's look at some of the ways you found to solve this problem."

Min Lee volunteered first. "I got 60. I know that 50% of 80 is 40. 25% is half of 50%. Since 50% was 40, then 25% must be half of that or 20. Then I added 40 and 20. I got 60."

"How many of you used Min Lee's method?" Several students raised their hands.

"Who can tell us another way to look at the problem?"

Jack responded. "I know that 10% of 80 is 8. In order to get 70%, I multiplied 8×7 and got 56. But I still need 5% more. I thought 5% is half of 10%, so 5% must be 4. By adding 56 and 4, I got 60, the same as Min Lee."

Several students indicated they were unclear, so Jack repeated the strategy elaborating on his procedure and stopping after each step to clarify.

Stephanie volunteered another method. "75% is the same as $\frac{3}{4}$. I divided 80 into fourths. Each fourth is 20. Three of them are 60."

"I changed 75% to 0.75 and multiplied. 0.75×80 is 60." offered Jose.

As students present their strategies, there should be opportunities to compare the methods to see how they are alike and how they are different. Students should be asked to consider which strategies they think worked best with the particular problem and why.

Discussions like the one above are rich in reasoning and proof. Whether a student is explaining his answer to the class or listening to the explanation of another to see if it makes sense, reasoning skills are being employed. The time spent on conversations like these, with thoughtful questions posed by the teacher to guide the discussion, is invaluable.

Middle School Communication

WHETHER BETWEEN TEACHER AND STUDENT, between a pair of students, or among groups of students, the communication skills of reading, writing, and listening and speaking provide the means for sharing ideas and promoting mathematical understanding. As students express their ideas through oral and written language, they have an opportunity to clarify their thinking and reinforce their comprehension of the concepts they are working with. By listening to explanations given by their classmates, students are exposed to ideas they may not have thought of. This provides a greater network of connections among ideas and, in turn, enhances learning.

Ample opportunities to discuss mathematical ideas should be provided. One extremely effective technique that was described in the previous section on Reasoning and Proof involves presenting an interesting problem to the class, allowing time to solve the problem, and then asking students to explain how they solved the problem. Providing a forum for a number of different solutions to be presented and defended by students results in rich dialogue. There is a very high level of mental activity associated with social interaction of this nature. Students who are afforded opportunities to take part in these mathematical conversations on a regular basis learn more effectively how to reason and defend their answers. In the process, they also learn to communicate and to clarify and refine their ideas, which leads to deeper understanding.

Elementary teachers lay the groundwork for students to develop facility in communicating their thinking. Children in the primary grades are usually interested in conversing about mathematics with the teacher as well as with others. If children in grades K–2 have had sufficient opportunities to discuss mathematical ideas, they generally are pretty comfortable continuing that pattern in grades 3–5. But all that changes in the middle school years. This period is characterized socially by wanting to fit in. Students become hesitant to put their thinking in front of others for fear of being ridiculed. Because adolescents are highly social, it becomes essential to have them work in groups. This provides them with a structured forum for their social behavior and a sense of camaraderie.

In middle school, mathematics begins to become more abstract. New concepts still need to be introduced conceptually, but students need to move from concrete representations to symbolic notation more quickly. Effective communication of ideas becomes even more important.

This portion of a 7th grade lesson offers an example of how communication was effectively used to develop an understanding of how surface area can vary for a fixed volume. Each student received 8 unit cubes and the class was led through an oral review of surface area and volume through a series of questions.

> **What is the volume of each cube?**
> **What is the total volume of the cubes?**
> **What is the surface area of each cube?**
> **What is the total surface area of the cubes?**

Students were then directed to arrange the 8 cubes in a 2×4 shape. Questions directed their attention to the concept being developed.

> **What is the volume of the figure you made with your cubes? Explain.**
> **Is the total surface area still 48 square units? Explain.**

As students responded to the questions, there was an opportunity to assess their ability to apply the definitions and figure volume and surface area. Any misunderstandings could be immediately addressed and corrected. Information could be expanded upon.

The lesson went on to have students work in pairs to explore other configurations using the 8 cubes and to find their surface areas and volumes and record their findings. A class discussion was held to compare the results. This led to a discussion about what configuration produced the greatest surface area and the least surface area for the same volume. Students went on to explore how symbolic representation could be used to express those relationships.

This approach allowed students to investigate a problem on a conceptual level with concrete objects and communicate understanding of the concepts involved before moving to symbolic representation. They had an opportunity to work together and communicate their ideas with each other as they investigated solutions. Their findings were then discussed in a larger group and there were opportunities to clarify, affirm, and reinforce understanding.

Putting ideas on paper is another means of helping students organize their thinking. The act of writing something down causes a student to reflect on ideas and refine them before committing that thinking to paper. Often, at the end of a lesson students will be asked to communicate what they learned in the problem or investigation they have just completed. This written reflection can be an important tool for teachers in assessing their students' mathematical understanding. Words, pictures, numbers, and symbols are all important parts of written communication that students have at their disposal, and middle school students are becoming much more adept at using mathematical symbols to communicate their thinking. Many teachers use journal writing as a way for students to relate what they know about mathematics.

Students in grades 6–8 should be provided with regular opportunities to use both oral and written language and to share mathematical ideas with their teachers and peers on a daily basis. This exchange will challenge students to reexamine or refine their thinking and will affirm understanding. This process is essential to internalizing mathematics.

Middle School Connections

MAKING CONNECTIONS IN MATHEMATICS is a three-fold process. First, connections are made when one mathematical idea is used to build another. Second, connections are made among different mathematical ideas. Third, connections are made between mathematics and contexts outside the field of mathematics.

Because mathematics is an integrated discipline, treating it as a whole body of knowledge and focusing on the connections that occur naturally adds dimension to ideas and concepts. How is counting related to addition, addition to subtraction, addition to multiplication, multiplication to area? A cohesive curriculum that is clearly articulated from pre-kindergarten through the twelfth grade, one that connects the mathematical ideas within each grade as well as the mathematics between grade levels, is critical if those connections are to take place.

Making connections to prior mathematical experiences is vital for the understanding of how mathematical ideas build on one another. Teachers need to know what mathematics students learned previously in order to build on that knowledge. In a given unit of study, attention should be paid to ensure that mathematics concepts build upon one another from day to day in a coherent manner. Teachers should also be aware of what their students will be studying in subsequent grades so they can lay the foundations for obvious connections to further studies.

Mathematics permeates other curriculum areas and it is found in the everyday experience outside of school as well. The use of shapes and patterns is prevalent in art and architecture; measurement skills and classification skills are important in science; measurement skills and knowledge of fractions are utilized in cooking and in building models; and measurement skills, data gathering, and statistics are applied in the social sciences.

In middle school, students build on the mathematical foundation laid in elementary school. The concepts of fractions, decimals, and percents were introduced informally in grades K–5, but in grades 6–8, the relationships among these forms take on greater focus. Students become aware of the similarities and differences in these representations and learn which is appropriate for a particular situation. Proportional reasoning and algebraic thinking are also major areas of study. The number work developed in intermediate grades is extended to include work with integers.

Computing with integers is a new topic for middle school students, one that can be connected to the study of number relationships that students encountered in elementary school. The number line, something all students have had experience with, is a helpful tool for modeling addition and subtraction with integers.

There are countless ways to make connections with the mathematics studied in the middle grades. For example, students enjoy taking surveys of their peers' preferences in food, music, movies, and games. This can be connected to collecting, organizing, and displaying this data in a way that makes sense, important skills that help students to better understand and interpret information presented in the world around them. Analyzing the data gathered from these surveys can be connected to interesting statistical problems. The teacher might pose the questions or have students generate their own.

Calculating the cost of having a class party that includes refreshments, prizes for games, and paper products is another relevant problem for students in grades 6–8. Such an activity makes connections to the real world and to students' estimation skills, their understanding of ratios, and their knowledge of operations with fractions and decimals. Working in teams, students can generate a menu and figure out how to adhere to a given budget. This kind of problem also encourages cost comparisons among various brands.

It is important for teachers to be conscious of connections that can be made in mathematics and to weave those connections into daily practice. When students are able to connect mathematical ideas both inside and outside of the classroom, they begin to see mathematics as a cohesive body of knowledge.

Middle School Representation

REPRESENTATIONS PROVIDE VEHICLES FOR EXPRESSING and internalizing mathematical thought. They include physical objects, pictures, and symbols; and they encompass mental images, words, and ideas as well. Representation is a critical component in shaping the way students access, understand, express, and utilize mathematical ideas

Representations can be formal or informal. Examples of formal representations are the conventional symbols, graphs, diagrams, and so on traditionally introduced in school mathematics. More informal forms are often invented by students as a way of making sense of mathematical ideas and communicating those ideas to classmates or the teacher. Connecting to these informal forms will facilitate a meaningful transition to thinking and communicating in the language of mathematics.

As teachers design lessons, choosing the type of representations they feel will best help students understand a concept becomes an important consideration. What shared mathematical language is needed to effectively communicate ideas? What manipulatives or models will be appropriate? How will students record their understanding of the concept? When is it appropriate to move from physical to symbolic representations?

Students at the middle-school level use informal methods to help them interpret ideas that are more complex. For example, before introducing the formula for finding the volume of rectangular solids, a teacher might assign the following task to groups of four:

> **Using centimeter cubes, build a variety of rectangular solids. Record the length, width, and height of each one you build. Also, record the number of cubes used to build each figure.**

As the students build their solids and record information, the teacher can move among the groups asking questions. The lesson can conclude with a discussion about the relationships between the dimensions of the solids and the number of cubes used to build them. Students share the charts they made which clearly show that the number of centimeters used was equal to the length times the width times the height of the solid.

Rectangular Solids

Length	Width	Height	Total Cubes
2	2	2	8
3	2	2	12
3	3	2	18
3	3	3	27
4	3	2	24
4	4	2	32
4	4	3	48
4	4	4	64

The students are then ready to be presented with the symbolic representation $V = l \times w \times h$, the formula used to find the volume of a rectangular solid.

In this example, using physical representation by building models provides direct experience with the relationships among the length, width, and height and the volume of a figure. This allows students to establish a mental representation of the relationships, so the abstract equation will make sense to them. These students are much more likely to remember the formula.

Conclusion

The process standards are not an end in, and of, themselves. Rather, they provide the advanced organizers, or plan, for lessons that present important mathematics content. Seeing connections among mathematical topics enables students to reason and make sense of new ideas and problem-solving situations they encounter. Through the process of communication, students are able to represent these new ideas either formally or informally.

Just as process standards are interrelated, so are the process and content standards. For true mathematical thinking and learning to occur, both process and content need to be skillfully woven into and through each lesson. That is the goal to work toward.

Standard 1 **Number and Operation**

AT THE SIXTH GRADE LEVEL, number and operation includes work with number theory topics, ratio and proportion, exponents, and the relationships between fractions, decimals, and percents. Our lessons are derived from these important topics, and include a lesson that focuses on prime and composite numbers, a lesson that develops the concept of ratio, a lesson that introduces exponents, and a lesson that relates fractions, decimals, and percents.

Three lessons model how the process standards can be used to teach content. A fourth lesson is a hypothetical textbook lesson that we have revised to be more standards based. These four lessons do not represent the entire curriculum, but rather provide glimpses of how, with a more concentrated effort to incorporate the process standards, better mathematics teaching and learning can be achieved.

One lesson we have chosen focuses on the concept of ratio. Making connections and different representations are what drive this lesson. Students make connections to what they know about fractions and extend their knowledge of part-to-whole relationships to include part-to-part and whole-to-part relationships. Students realize that ratios can be written using the word "to," with a colon, or as a fraction.

Another lesson we have chosen is one that focuses on the number theory topic of how to classify numbers as prime or composite. Rather than simply defining prime and composite and having students practice classifying, representation and reasoning and proof serve as the driving force of this lesson to help students visualize and draw their own conclusions about what separates a prime number from a composite number.

A third lesson we have chosen introduces students to exponents. Connections, representation, and communication motivate this lesson that is often reduced to defining terms and practicing. Students often develop misconceptions and erroneous ways of thinking as they work with exponents. By providing opportunities for students to discuss their thinking, much of this can be resolved before it becomes ingrained. Connections are made as exponential notation is used to represent the repeated multiplication of one factor just as multiplication represents the repeated addition of one addend.

The hypothetical textbook lesson that we have chosen to revise relates fractions, decimals, and percents. Converting between forms is often a mechanical process. By incorporating connections and reasoning and proof, students relate the different forms to their own experiences, realizing that there are times when one form may be better than the other two. By doing so, they are better able to develop methods for converting between forms.

Standard 1 Lessons

Investigating Ratio

Understanding Prime and Composite

Understanding Exponents

Relating Fractions, Decimals, and Percents

Investigating Ratio

Introduction

Objective → Students will explore and understand the concept of ratio.

Context → Students have experienced number relationships such as part to whole, as in fractions. They have also used comparison when analyzing number relationships, as in numerical patterns. This is an introduction to the concept of ratio; students will go on to learn about proportion.

NCTM Standards Focus

This standards-based lesson draws on the students' intuitive notions of fractions and patterns to help them understand different ratio relationships. They look at all the ways ratio can be expressed with three given numbers and think about what each ratio represents. They then examine ratios to gain further insight about relationships that exist among the items.

Representation Students analyze a situation and find different ways to represent its components in ratio form. They express ratio as part to whole, whole to part, and part to part.

Connections Students reflect on the different ways to represent ratio numerically when dealing with a part-to-whole situation. They build on this knowledge to show part-to-part relationships. They connect their knowledge of fractions to the new concept of ratio.

Communication In their groups, students discuss ways in which their language skills help them approach different situations involving ratio. They describe relationships in words and in mathematical terms. Discussing their findings affords an opportunity to listen to their classmates' thinking and adapt their own methods when they find something that makes more sense.

Teaching Plan

Materials → Student pages 22–23

DRAW THREE RECTANGLES AND FOUR TRIANGLES on the board. *What are some ways to describe the figures drawn on the board?* If students suggest that there are 3 rectangles and 4 triangles, ask them how they might describe the figures in relationship to one another, such as "four of the seven shapes are triangles."

Demonstrate that there are three ways to use numbers to record the word description; 4:7, 4 to 7, or in fraction form as $\frac{4}{7}$. Discuss that each of the notations is used to represent a *ratio*, a comparison of two quantities. Point out that frequently the fraction form is preferred when expressing ratios.

Explain that all fractions are ratios; fractions compare parts to wholes. Make clear that all ratios deal with comparisons; however, not all ratios are fractions. A ratio can also be used to compare one part or group to another as when comparing the number of rectangular shapes to the number of triangular shapes.

Allow time for students to find and record as many ways as possible of comparing the figures drawn on the board. Encourage students to express the ratios they find first verbally, and then mathematically, using all three forms of notation.

- ratio of triangles to the total shapes; 4 to 7, 4:7, $\frac{4}{7}$
- ratio of rectangles to total shapes; 3 to 7, 3:7, $\frac{3}{7}$
- ratio of rectangles to triangles; 3 to 4, 3:4, $\frac{3}{4}$
- ratio of triangles to rectangles; 4 to 3, 4:3, $\frac{4}{3}$;
- ratio of total shapes to rectangles; 7 to 3, 7:3, $\frac{7}{3}$
- ratio of total shapes to triangles; 7 to 4, 7:4, $\frac{7}{4}$

What Might Happen . . . What to Do

Students might have difficulty finding all the ratios that can be expressed with the three numbers 3, 4, and 7. Have the students use manipulatives to represent the shapes. Using concrete models to explore ratios visually reinforces the part-to-part relationships and the part-to-whole relationships.

Have students determine whether a ratio they have already expressed can be reversed. *What is the ratio of triangles to total shapes? What is the ratio of total shapes to triangles?* Students should see that the numbers are the same but that the order in which the ratio is expressed has been reversed.

Ask students to solve another problem to check their understanding. Tell students that pencils are sold in packages at a ratio of 5 designer pencils to 7 plain pencils. *What would be the fewest pencils in a package? Would there be more designer pencils or more plain pencils in the package? What ratios can you write for those quantities?* Write the ratios on the board as students give them. For each ratio, ask the rest of the class to agree or disagree.

Now present a situation that will allow students to explore the relationships that can be determined based on ratios. Explain that you have a bag of red and blue marbles and that the ratio of red marbles to blue marbles is 2 to 3. *If there are five marbles in the bag, how many are red?* (2) *How many are blue?* (3) *Without changing the ratio, if the number of red marbles is doubled, how many blue marbles should there be?* (6) *How many marbles will there be in all?* (10) *If there are 50 marbles in the bag, how many should be red?* (20) *How many should be blue?* (30)

Have students work together in groups of two to four and observe them as they answer questions. If some students have difficulties getting started, remind them that the ratio of red marbles to blue marbles is 2 to 3. Ask questions about colors and numbers and the order in which they occur in the sentence, without giving the solution.

EXTEND STUDENTS' UNDERSTANDING of the relationships that exist within the ratio given for the bag of marbles. *How many red marbles could be in the bag?* (Any even number) *How would the corresponding number of blue marbles be determined?* (It would be the multiple of three. The multiple would correspond to the number of red marbles divided by two.) *Regardless of the number of marbles, what statements would be true about the marbles in the bag?* (The total number would be a multiple of 5; $\frac{2}{5}$ will be red, $\frac{3}{5}$ will be blue.)

Continue to ask questions that help increase students' understanding of ratio relationships. *Will there always be an odd number of blue marbles?* (No. An even multiple of 3 will produce an even number.) *What is the difference between one quantity in the ratio and the other? Does the difference remain the same as increases are made to the quantities? Explain.*

Since the questions ask for relationships rather than exact answers, some students may choose to model an exact situation and then extend it. Allow students to model situations, but then encourage them to generalize from those examples to answer questions. Have groups communicate their findings to the class.

Answers

Page 22

1. $\frac{1}{3}$
2. $\frac{100}{1}$
3. $\frac{8}{32}$
4. $\frac{1}{10}$
5. $\frac{1}{16}$
6. $\frac{3}{6}$ (triangles to squares), $\frac{6}{3}$ (squares to triangles), $\frac{3}{9}$ (triangles to total shapes), $\frac{9}{3}$ (total shapes to triangles), $\frac{6}{9}$ (squares to total shapes), $\frac{9}{6}$ (total shapes to squares)
7. $\frac{14}{24}$ (gold to total), $\frac{24}{14}$ (total to gold), $\frac{10}{24}$ (other metals to total), $\frac{24}{10}$ (total to other metals), $\frac{14}{10}$ (gold to other metals), $\frac{10}{14}$ (other metals to gold)
8. $\frac{6}{4}$ (red beans to white beans), $\frac{4}{6}$ (white to red), $\frac{6}{10}$ (red to total), $\frac{10}{6}$ (total to red), $\frac{4}{10}$ (white to total), $\frac{10}{4}$ (total to white)
9. $\frac{14}{8}$ (front windows to back windows), $\frac{8}{14}$ (back to front), $\frac{14}{22}$ (front to total), $\frac{22}{14}$ (total to front), $\frac{8}{22}$ (back to total), $\frac{22}{8}$ (total to back)
10. $\frac{4}{16}$ (tomato paste to tomato sauce), $\frac{16}{4}$ (sauce to paste), $\frac{4}{20}$ (paste to total mixture), $\frac{20}{4}$ (total to paste), $\frac{16}{20}$ (sauce to total), $\frac{20}{16}$ (total to sauce)

Conclude the lesson by asking students to offer different situations they have encountered that involve ratios. Have them explain how knowing about ratio relationships might be useful and provide an example.

Student Pages

Student page 22 gives students opportunities to write ratios. Student page 23 asks interpretive questions about ratios.

Assessment

As students explored different ways to express ratios, there were opportunities to see how well they understood ratios as part-to-whole and part-to-part relationships. Students used critical thinking as they analyzed number relationships and made generalizations. Their responses showed how well they understood both the relationships between different numbers and the ways of representing these relationships.

NCTM Standards Summary

Students connected their prior knowledge of fractions as part-to-whole relationships, to relationships expressed as ratios. Using this relationship, they went on to explore part-to-part relationships as ratios. They connected verbal expressions to mathematical symbols using the standard of representation. They communicated their insights with group members and classmates. They discussed ideas about ratio with each other and determined which approaches made sense.

Page 23

1. 4, 2; $\frac{4}{2}$ (numerals beginning with t to numerals beginning with s), $\frac{2}{4}$ (numerals beginning with s to those beginning with t), $\frac{4}{12}$ (numerals beginning with t to total), $\frac{12}{4}$ (total to t), $\frac{2}{12}$ (numerals beginning with s to total), $\frac{12}{10}$ (total to s).
2. $\frac{6}{4}$; more sedans than utility vehicles rode over the bridge; sedans are 6 out of 10 cars; utility vehicles are 4 out of 10; 68.
3. Total sheets in the pad should be a multiple of 4; $\frac{1}{4}$ of the sheets are white; $\frac{3}{4}$ of the sheets are colored.
4. more girls, $\frac{4}{7}$ of the students are girls; $\frac{3}{7}$ of the students are boys; there are fewer boys; total number of students is divisible by 7.
5. $\frac{3}{6}$ are odd; $\frac{3}{6}$ are even; ratio of even to odd is $\frac{3}{3}$; $\frac{1}{3}$.
6. Answers will vary.

Name

Investigating Ratio

Write the ratios.

1. What is the ratio of a foot to a yard?

2. What is the ratio of meters to centimeters?

3. What is the ratio of ounces in a cup to ounces in a quart?

4. What is the ratio of deciliters to a liter?

5. What is the ratio of ounces to a pound?

Write six ratios for each problem. Write what each ratio represents.

6. There are 3 triangles and 6 squares in the pattern.

7. Pure gold is 24 karats. Most jewelry is 14-karat gold and the rest is other metals.

8. There are 2 types of beans in a bag. There are 6 red beans to 4 white beans.

9. In a townhouse, 14 windows face the front and 8 windows face the back.

10. The recipe calls for 4 ounces of tomato paste and 16 ounces of tomato sauce.

Name

Investigating Ratio

Answer the questions.

1. An analog clock has 12 numerals on its face.
   - How many of the numerals begin with the letter *t*?
   - How many of the numerals begin with the letter *s*?
   - What ratios can you write for these numbers?
   - What does each ratio represent?

2. Between 8 a.m. and 9 a.m., there were 4 utility vehicles for every 6 sedans crossing the bridge.
   - What is the ratio of sedans to utility vehicles?
   - What do you know about the total number of vehicles crossing the bridge between 8 and 9 a.m.?
   - 102 sedans crossed the bridge beteween 8 and 9 a.m. How many utility vehicles crossed the bridge during that time?

3. In a pad of drawing paper, the ratio of sheets of colored paper to sheets of white paper is 3:1.
   - What do you know about the total number of sheets in the pad?
   - What fraction of sheets of paper in the pad are white?
   - What fraction of sheets of paper in the pad are colored?

4. In the school, the ratio of boys to girls is $\frac{3}{4}$.
   - Are there more boys or girls in the school?
   - What ratio describes the number of girls to the total number of students?
   - What ratio describes the number of boys to the total number of students?
   - What do you know about the total number of students in the school?

5. A number cube has 6 faces with the numbers 1 through 6.
   - What is the ratio of odd-numbered faces to total faces?
   - What is the ratio of even-numbered faces to total faces?
   - What is the ratio of even faces to odd?
   - What is the ratio of the faces that have numbers greater than 5 to those having 4 or greater?

6. Write a situation that shows a ratio. Provide questions similar to those on this page.

Understanding Prime and Composite

Introduction

Objective → Students will understand prime and composite numbers.

Context → Students have learned the difference between odd and even numbers. They will use what they have learned to work with prime factorizations, greatest common factors, and least common multiples.

NCTM Standards Focus

Most lessons that introduce prime and composite numbers do so by simply defining the two terms and having students classify certain numbers. For students who do not yet have a solid understanding of factors, a lesson of this nature may be difficult. A more standards-based lesson would develop the concepts in greater depth and with a visual representation, rather than with just an abstract definition. Incorporating the following three process standards into the lesson will help students better understand prime and composite numbers.

Reasoning and Proof Students separate numbers into two types: prime and composite. They use visual representation of the two types of numbers to confirm that their conclusions are correct.

Representation Students use square tiles to create visual representations of prime and composite numbers. They form rectangles to represent the factors of a number. Then they separate numbers into primes and composites based on whether only one rectangle or multiple rectangles can be formed to represent a given number.

Connections Once students have separated numbers into the two types using visual representation, they can make connections to the terms prime and composite. Students use their knowledge of multiplication and division to make connections to prime and composite numbers.

Teaching Plan

Materials → Student pages 28–29; 465 square tiles; chart on page 25

DISPLAY A RECTANGULAR ARRANGEMENT of 15 tiles and ask the class how many tiles are used. Ask how they know. When the response is that there are 3 rows of 5 tiles, ask what multiplication problem this represents. Point out that one rectangle represents 3×5 and 5×3. Remind students that 3 and 5 are factors of 15.

Write the chart shown on page 25 on the board or overhead. Have students work together in pairs or groups. Give one group 10 tiles and assign them the numbers 2 through 10. Tell them that for each number, they must use that many tiles to make their rectangles. For example, if they are working with the number 6, they must find as many ways as possible to create rectangles using 6 tiles. Give the next group 15 tiles and ask them to use the tiles to make as many rectangles as possible for each number from 11 through 15. Continue in this manner so that groups of students work with all of the numbers on the chart.

Number of Tiles	Make Rectangles for These Numbers
10	2–10
15	11–15
20	16–20
24	21–24
28	25–28
32	29–32
36	33–36
40	37–40
44	41–44
48	45–48
52	49–52
56	53–56
60	57–60

This activity will provide students with a visual representation of prime and composite numbers. It will also help students separate numbers into those that have exactly two factors and those that have more than two factors.

USING THE RECORDING SHEET on student page 28, have students record the number of tiles they started with, the dimensions of each rectangle created, the total number of rectangles created for each number, and the total number of factors for that number.

What Might Happen . . . What to Do

There are two common errors that students might make during the activity. First, they might count 3 × 5 and 5 × 3 as two different rectangles. If so, they could list 3 and 5 as factors twice. Second, they might not realize that a square is a rectangle. As a result, they might consider some square numbers as prime. If you observe students making either of these errors, discuss them with the group or the class.

Each group of students should examine their data and write down their thoughts and observations about their findings before they share them with the class. Begin class discussion by compiling a list on the board showing the numbers 1–60, the total number of rectangles made for each number, and the total number of factors. Have students look back through their written thoughts and observations to see whether they are true for all of the numbers. This will help students connect what they noticed about their set of numbers to all of the numbers.

It is important that students focus on the goal of this lesson. *How many factors do the numbers with one rectangle have? What do you notice about the numbers that have exactly two factors?* (All are odd except for two.)

ASK STUDENTS TO SHARE their thoughts with the class and to come up with one or more general statements about the numbers. Students are using reasoning and proof at several levels when they connect their initial thoughts and observations with the results of the rest of the class and then make generalizing statements.

Students may come up with one or more of the following observations:

- All of the numbers that have only one rectangle have two factors, except 1.
- The numbers that have only two factors have only one possible rectangle.
- Two is the only even number that has a total of 2 factors.
- All other even numbers have more than one rectangle.

Now make the connections to the important terms of the lesson. Define PRIME numbers as those numbers that have exactly two factors. *What are the two factors of a prime number?* (The number itself and 1) Define COMPOSITE numbers as those numbers that have more than two factors. A good question to ask to help students realize the distinction is: *Can a number be both prime and composite?* (No) *Why not?* (A prime number has only two factors; a composite number has more than two factors.) Give students time to ask any questions they may have.

ASK STUDENTS HOW THEY COULD use the hundred chart on student page 28 to figure out which numbers are prime. If necessary, suggest that they think about the multiples of numbers. Following this discussion, introduce students to the Sieve of Eratosthenes. Since 1 is not prime, students can start with 2. They circle 2, then cross out all the multiples of 2. They circle the next number that is not crossed out, 3, and cross out all the multiples of 3. Students circle the next number that is not crossed out, 5, and cross out the multiples of 5. They continue in this fashion until all the numbers have been either circled or crossed out. The circled numbers are the prime numbers. Students can compare this list with the list from their earlier activity. *Can you verify the generalizations you made in the earlier activity with the numbers 61 through 100?*

At this point, you might want to reinforce aspects of the lesson. *Why is 2 the only even prime number?* (All other even numbers have 2 and half the number as factors, in addition to 1 and the number itself.) *Should 1 be considered a prime number?* (No, it has only one factor—itself.)

Extension

Point out that any even composite number can be expressed as the sum of two prime numbers. Have students check to see if this is true for all of the even composite numbers up to 100. For example, the composite number 32 can be expressed as the sum of the two primes, 3 + 29, or 13 + 19.

Student Pages

Student page 28 features a recording chart for students to use with the activity, as well as a hundred chart for students to use for the Sieve of Eratosthenes activity.

Student page 29 provides some practice with the concepts of this lesson. To help assess the depth of their understanding, students are asked both to identify a number as prime or composite and to explain what makes it prime or composite.

Assessment

During the activity, you observed students as they made their rectangles and wrote their observations. During the class discussion, you were able to see if students made the connection between the number of factors a number has and whether it is prime or composite. The suggested questions also provided good opportunities to assess students' understanding of the concept of prime and composite numbers. The exercises on student page 29 provide some questions with which to assess students individually.

NCTM Standards Summary

This lesson focused on the NCTM process standards reasoning and proof, representation, and connections. Students made observations, refined their thoughts, and then made generalizations based on class results. This helped students use their reasoning skills and reinforced the importance of being able to explain their reasoning.

Through using tiles to create visual representations of prime and composite numbers, students had the chance to define these numbers for themselves and to make connections between each term and the concept of factors. The exercises reinforced these connections by asking students to relate each term back to the activity and to connect their description of a number, prime or composite, with the number of factors it has.

Answers

Page 28

Answers may vary.

Page 29

1. composite; sample answer: has more than two factors
2. composite; sample answer: can make more than one rectangle
3. prime; sample answer: has only two factors, 1 and 17
4. composite; sample answer: has more than two factors
5. prime; sample answer: can make only one rectangle
6. prime; sample answer: has only two factors
7. neither; sample answer: 1 has only one factor; primes have two; and composites have more than two
8. Only one rectangle is possible for prime numbers; two or more rectangles are possible for composite numbers; examples will vary.

Name

Understanding Prime and Composite

Record your findings about the numbers.

Recording Chart

Number of Tiles	Dimensions of Rectangles	Total Number of Rectangles	Total Number of Factors

Use the hundred chart to find prime numbers.

Hundred Chart

1	2	3	4	5	6	7	8	9	10
11	12	13	14	15	16	17	18	19	20
21	22	23	24	25	26	27	28	29	30
31	32	33	34	35	36	37	38	39	40
41	42	43	44	45	46	47	48	49	50
51	52	53	54	55	56	57	58	59	60
61	62	63	64	65	66	67	68	69	70
71	72	73	74	75	76	77	78	79	80
81	82	83	84	85	86	87	88	89	90
91	92	93	94	95	96	97	98	99	100

Name

Understanding Prime and Composite

For numbers 1–6, determine whether each number is prime or composite. Give a reason for your answer.

1. 36

2. 45

3. 17

4. 93

5. 79

6. 2

7. Is 1 considered to be a prime number, a composite number, or neither? Explain.

8. Explain how making rectangles from square tiles can help you define and identify prime numbers and composite numbers. Show an example to support your explanation.

Understanding Exponents

Introduction

Objective → Students will understand that exponents are used to shorten the notation for repeated multiplication of one factor. Students will be able to evaluate expressions with exponents using a calculator.

Context → This is an introductory lesson for exponents. Students will go on to use exponents in the order of operations and in variable expressions.

NCTM Standards Focus

Exponents are often presented as being unrelated to any other mathematical knowledge that students have. When first working with exponents, students form several misconceptions about how to think about them. By better incorporating the following process standards, students will be able to make some connections, discuss different misconceptions, and learn how to represent exponential expressions on a calculator in order to evaluate them.

Connections Students relate using exponents as a way to show repeated multiplication to when they learned multiplication as a way to show repeated addition. They make connections to the terms "squared" and "cubed."

Representation Students learn how to write exponential notation. They learn how to enter and evaluate exponential expressions on a calculator.

Communication Students learn and use new vocabulary. Through discussion of students' misconceptions, they are able to refine their own thinking about exponents.

Teaching Plan

Materials → Student pages 34–35; calculators

BEGIN THE LESSON WITH A BRIEF REVIEW of the notion that multiplication is simply a more efficient way to express the repeated addition of one addend. You might write an expression such as $4 + 4 + 4 + 4 + 4 + 4 + 4 + 4$ on the board and ask students to evaluate. Discuss their methods. Some students might think 4, 8, 12, 16, 20, 24, 28, 32, while others might count 8 fours being added, which is 32. Help students make the connection that multiplication is the same as repeated addition. Do another example or two to reinforce the point.

You could also approach this as an oral exercise. Say an expression, such as "$4 + 4 + 4 + 4 + 4 + 4 + 4 + 4$" quickly, so that most students do not have time to keep a running tally in their heads. Ask the class for the result. After a couple of moments, say "For those of you who didn't catch all that, I said it 8 times." Most hands should now be raised.

NOW ASK THE CLASS TO CONSIDER changing the "+" signs to "×." Write $4 \times 4 \times 4 \times 4 \times 4 \times 4$ on the board. *Now we have a repeated multipli-*

cation. Before we evaluate it, is there a more efficient way to write it? Just as there was a shorter way to write a repeated addition, is there a shorter way to write a repeated multiplication? This leads directly into the representation of writing exponential notation.

Write 4^6 on the board. Ask students what they think each number represents (4 is the factor, 6 is the number of times it is multiplied). Now that students have an informal idea of what the base and exponent represent, good communication and making strong connections suggest that it is an appropriate time to introduce the vocabulary.

Define *base* as the factor that is being repeatedly multiplied. Define *exponent* as telling the number of times the base is to be used as a factor. Model for students how the expression is read: "Four raised to the sixth power."

PRESENT ANOTHER EXAMPLE, such as 2^{10}. Ask students how the expression should be read (two to the tenth power). Have them identify the base (2) and the exponent (10). *What does the expression mean?* (2 is used as a factor 10 times) Have students write the repeated multiplication.

Ask students how much they think 2^{10} is. One of the most common misconceptions students have is that they simply multiply the base and the exponent—in this case, 2×10. One way to address this is to raise the issue before it becomes a problem. Ask students if they think that 20 is a reasonable answer. *How would 20 be obtained?* Let students discuss these points. By having open communication here, a common misconception can hopefully be avoided.

How can 2^{10} or 4^6 be evaluated? One way is to simply multiply the factors. $2 \times 2 = 4$, $4 \times 2 = 8$, $8 \times 2 = 16$, $16 \times 2 = 32$, $32 \times 2 = 64$, $64 \times 2 = 128$, $128 \times 2 = 256$, $256 \times 2 = 512$, $512 \times 2 = 1024$. Also, $4 \times 4 = 16$, $16 \times 4 = 64$, $64 \times 4 = 256$, $256 \times 4 = 1024$, $1024 \times 4 = 4096$.

Would you want to rely on this method for evaluating any exponential expression? Why or why not? You want students to realize that this method is certainly time-consuming, especially if the exponent is greater. Also, the answers get to be rather large, especially for greater bases, which makes mental math more difficult.

Suggest that calculators know how to evaluate powers. To allow representation of exponents, many calculators have either a caret key (^) or an x^y key (or both). To evaluate 2^{10}, press 2 (^ or x^y) 10 (= or Enter). To evaluate 4^6, press 4 (^ or x^y) 6 (= or Enter).

Write the expressions 2^3 and 3^2 on the board. Ask students if they think they are the same. Here are some things that you would like students to realize.

- The first is read "two to the third power" and the second is "three to the second power."
- Neither expression is 6.
- The first means 2 used as a factor 3 times, the second is 3 used as a factor 2 times.
- The first expression is 8, the second is 9.

From these two expressions, the terms "squared" and "cubed" come from a connection to geometry and measurement. "Squared" refers to the area of a square and "cubed" refers to the volume of a cube.

Tell students that another way to read "three to the second power" is "three squared." Show students a segment of length 3 units. Then draw a square with sides of length 3 units. The area is length × width, or 3 × 3, which is 3^2 or 3 "squared."

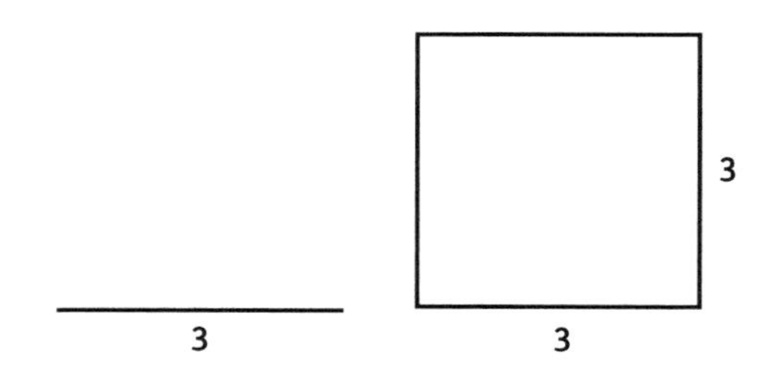

Tell students that another way to read "two to the third power" is "two cubed." Show students a segment of length 2 units. Then draw a cube with sides of length 2 units. The volume is length × width × height, or 2 × 2 × 2, which is 2^3, or 2 "cubed."

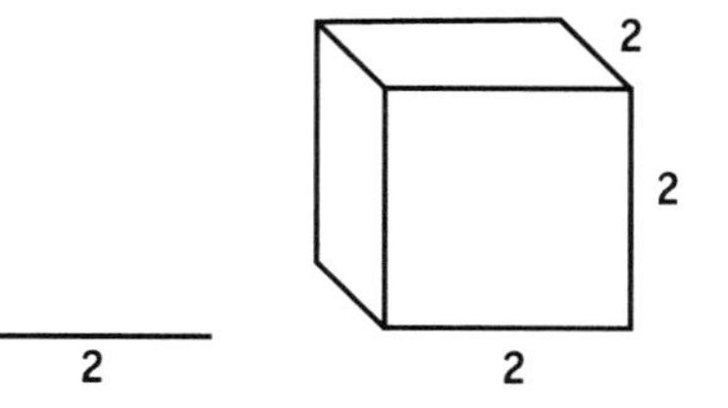

Ask students why there isn't a special name for raising to the fourth power or higher. (Cannot draw a four-dimensional figure.)

To reinforce the communication of the new vocabulary, present some oral exercises in which you ask students to evaluate expressions such as "7 squared" or "4 cubed."

TO FINISH THE LESSON, ask the following questions.

- *Is 3×4 the same as 3^4?* (No. The first is $3 + 3 + 3 + 3$ and the second is $3 \times 3 \times 3 \times 3$.)
- *Is exponential notation commutative? That is, we know $3 \times 4 = 4 \times 3$, but does $3^4 = 4^3$?* (No. $81 \neq 64$)
- (optional) *Can you think of one example in which it is?* ($4^2 = 2^4$)
- *Why haven't we seen 1 as an exponent?* (A written factor is understood to be one factor unless otherwise indicated. Writing the exponent 1 would be redundant.)
- *We have memorized the multiplication facts. Do we have to memorize the exponential facts?* (No. Numbers get too large very quickly. Calculators can help. Some will get to be memorized through repetition.)

Student Pages

Student page 34 provides practice writing repeated multiplication sentences in exponential form and exponential expressions as repeated multiplication. Student page 35 provides students an opportunity to evaluate exponential expressions mentally and with a calculator.

Assessment

Most of the assessment for this lesson was in the form of evaluating students' responses to the many questions posed and the discussions offered. The student pages may also be used to gauge individual progress.

NCTM Standards Summary

Students learned the important representations of exponential notation and how to enter exponential notation into a calculator. Students made many connections in this lesson, to geometry and measurement learning about "squared" and "cubed," informal ideas to correct vocabulary, and how exponential notation expresses repeated multiplication in the same way that multiplication represents repeated addition. Through many opportunities for communication, students were able to clarify the concepts and avoid some of the common misconceptions.

Answers

Page 34

1. a
2. c
3. a
4. 3^4
5. 2^6
6. 5^3
7. $4 \times 4 \times 4 \times 4 \times 4$
8. $3 \times 3 \times 3 \times 3 \times 3 \times 3 \times 3 \times 3$
9. $2 \times 2 \times 2 \times 2 \times 2 \times 2$
10. $10 \times 10 \times 10 \times 10$

Page 35

1. 8
2. 9
3. 125
4. 81
5. 64
6. 1
7. 64
8. 1000
9. 2
10. 36
11. Possible answer: 2^5 means 5 factors of 2, which is 32. 5^2 means 2 factors of 5, which is 25.
12. Possible answer: The student multiplied the base and the exponent. Explanations will vary.

Name ______________________________

Understanding Exponents

Circle the correct expression. Explain why you chose that answer.

1. $4 \times 4 \times 4 \times 4 \times 4 \times 4 =$
   a. 4^6　　b. 6^4　　c. 4^4

2. $3 \times 3 =$
   a. 3^3　　b. 3^9　　c. 3^2

3. $2 \times 2 \times 2 \times 2 \times 2 =$
   a. 2^5　　b. 5^2　　c. 2^2

Write each multiplication expression in exponential form.

4. $3 \times 3 \times 3 \times 3$

5. $2 \times 2 \times 2 \times 2 \times 2 \times 2$

6. $5 \times 5 \times 5$

Write each exponential expression as a repeated multiplication expression.

7. 4^5

8. 3^8

9. 2^6

10. 10^4

Name

Understanding Exponents

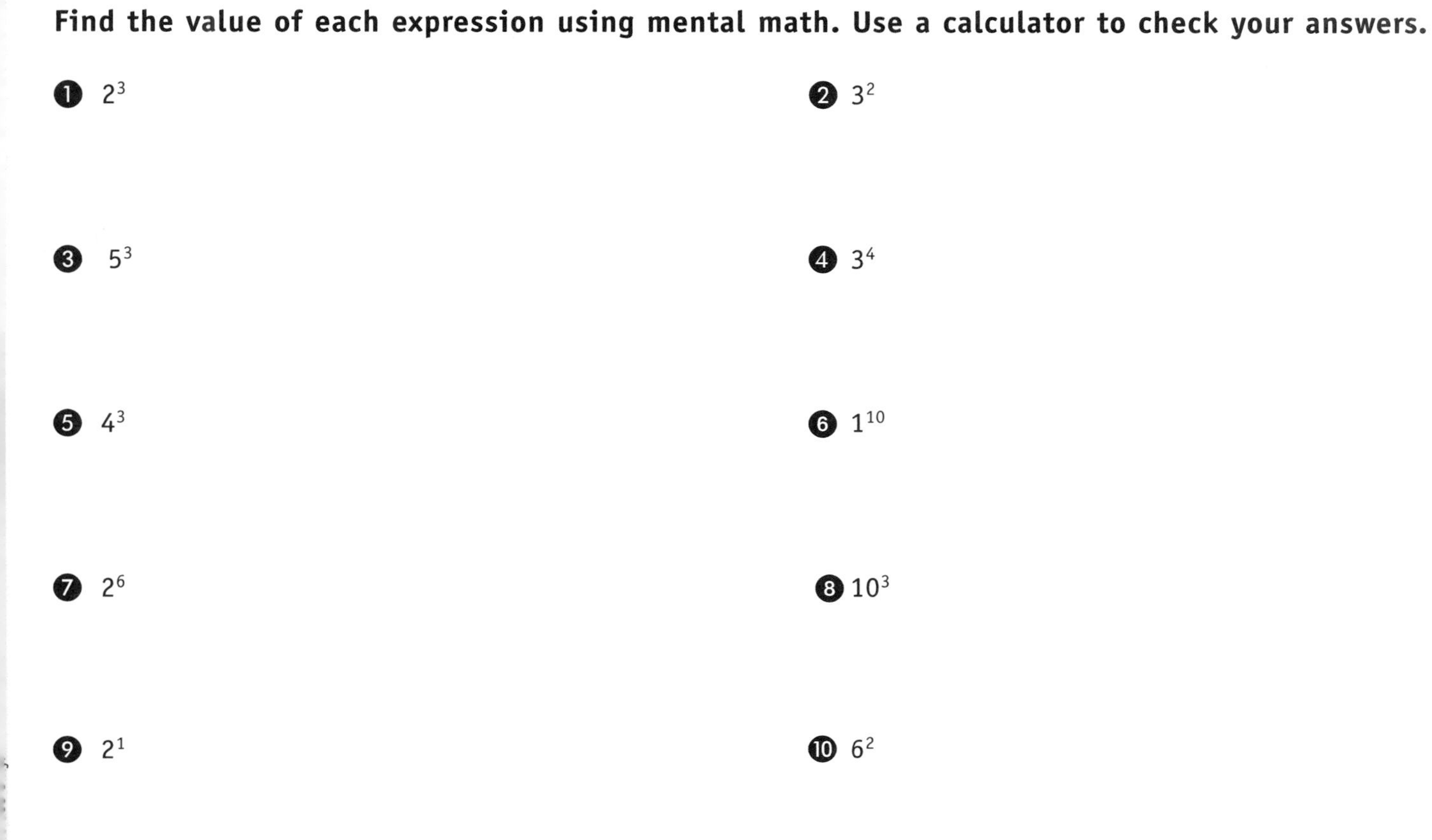

Find the value of each expression using mental math. Use a calculator to check your answers.

1. 2^3
2. 3^2
3. 5^3
4. 3^4
5. 4^3
6. 1^{10}
7. 2^6
8. 10^3
9. 2^1
10. 6^2
11. Explain why 2^5 and 5^2 do not give the same result.
12. A student evaluated 4^3 to be 12. What was the student's error? What would you do to help this student to understand?

Relating Fractions, Decimals, and Percents

Introduction

Objective → Students will convert among fractions, decimals, and percents.

Context → Students have discussed the meaning of percent and have written percents. Students have worked with equivalent fractions and fraction/decimal conversions. In the lesson that follows, students will solve percent problems, starting with finding percent of a number.

Relating Fractions, Decimals, and Percents

A percent can be shown as a fraction or a decimal.

2%	or	$\frac{2}{100}$	or	0.02
40%	or	$\frac{40}{100}$	or	0.40

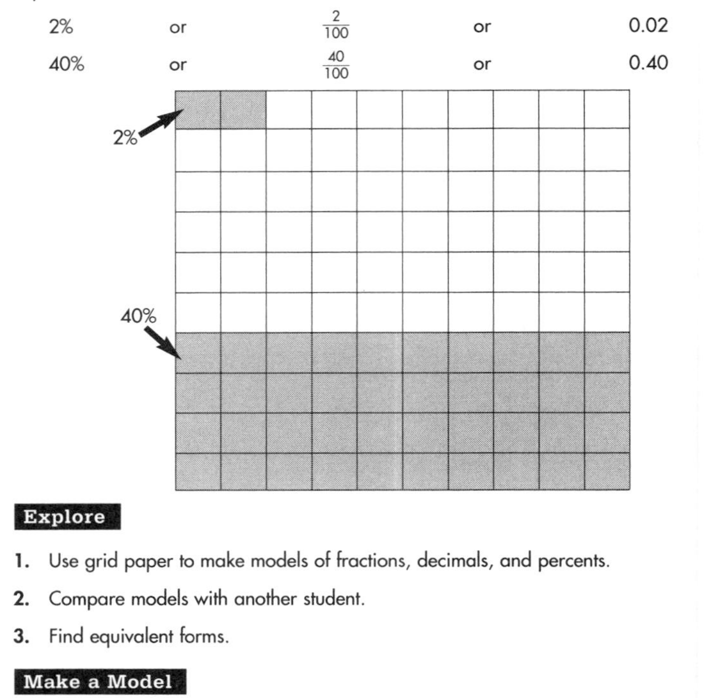

Explore

1. Use grid paper to make models of fractions, decimals, and percents.
2. Compare models with another student.
3. Find equivalent forms.

Make a Model

1. Use 10-by-10 grid paper to make models of these numbers.

a. 20%	b. $\frac{1}{4}$	c. 0.70	d. 40%	e. 0.25
f. $\frac{4}{5}$	g. 0.40	h. 35%	i. $\frac{2}{5}$	j. $\frac{7}{20}$

2. Do any of the models look the same?

NCTM Process Standards Analysis and Focus

The standards analysis examines how the process standards have been incorporated into the above lesson. By increasing the focus on three of the process standards, a more effective and meaningful lesson can be presented. The suggestions offered can help you to think about how this might be accomplished.

Connections The lesson presented has students notice mathematical connections among fractions, decimals, and percents. Opportunities to make real-world connections, however, are limited.

***Suggestion* → Establish connections to students' everyday experiences so that they see why it is important to be able to convert among fractions, decimals,**

Learn

Fraction to Percent
To change a fraction to a percent, write the fraction with a denominator of 100. Write the percent. $\frac{25}{100} = 25\%$

Decimal to Percent
Convert hundredths to percent. .25 = 25%

Practice

Write each decimal or fraction as a percent.

1. $\frac{2}{5}$ **2.** $\frac{200}{200}$ **3.** $\frac{9}{50}$ **4.** $\frac{50}{200}$ **5.** $\frac{1}{5}$ **6.** $\frac{21}{25}$

7. 0.03 **8.** 0.70 **9.** 0.87 **10.** 0.50 **11.** 0.98 **12.** 0.56

Write each percent as a decimal and a fraction. Express the fraction in lowest terms.

13. 32% **14.** 60% **15.** 71% **16.** 35% **17.** 18% **18.** 25%

19. 80% **20.** 92% **21.** 50% **22.** 36% **23.** 97% **24.** 4%

25. Critical Thinking What is the same as $\frac{3}{5}$? 0.6 or 6%?

26. Problem Solving An inspector in a factory found 3 bad parts after looking at 25 parts. What percentage of the parts were bad?

Journal

Make a table of some common percents to use when solving problems. Use 1%, 5%, 10%, 20%, 25%, 50%, 75%, and 100%. List their decimal and fractional equivalents.

and percents. By making connections to their prior knowledge, students will understand how the forms are related.

Reasoning and Proof The critical thinking problem in the lesson is a simple recognition exercise.

Suggestion → **Guide students to reason from the meaning of percent to develop methods for converting among forms. Students will apply these methods through understanding rather than through memorization.**

Representation Students make grid models of fractions, percents, and decimals.

Suggestion → **Have students represent fractions, percents, and decimals on hundred grids to help them visualize the relationships that exist between forms. Making hundred grid models will give them insight into methods that they can use to convert forms.**

Problem Solving An exercise labeled problem solving is a simple word problem.

Communication Students compare their models with those of a classmate. A journal activity involves making a table, although communicating ideas is not required.

The teaching plan that follows shows how the suggestions for increasing the focus on the process standards can be implemented.

Revised Teaching Plan

f.y.i.

Hundred grids can easily be made from graph paper. Distribute graph paper at the beginning of the lesson and instruct students to outline or cut out 10 × 10 squares.

Materials → Hundred grids, or plain graph paper

MOTIVATE THE NEED FOR CONVERSION BETWEEN FORMS by presenting the following situation: *Jason saw the same backpack in two stores. One store advertised* $\frac{1}{2}$ *off list price. The other store advertised 40% off list price.* Ask your students how Jason can decide which store offers the better price. Students should make the connection that converting and comparing fractions and percents is a practical skill that helps shoppers determine which store has the better deal.

Encourage students to suggest other real-life situations in which a number might have to be converted to a different form. Possibilities include buying ingredients for recipes or comparing distances. With each suggestion, have students articulate *why* it is necessary to know how to make conversions between forms. By emphasizing the practicality of this skill, you help students make connections vital to their understanding. *It's clear that there are times when it is important to be able to rename percents as fractions or decimals. Let's explore ways we can make those conversions.*

Have students work in pairs and use hundred grids. Tell them to use different colors to shade 40%, 0.20, and $\frac{2}{5}$ of the grid. When they finish, ask them to identify which parts are equal. After they conclude that 40% and $\frac{2}{5}$ are the same, ask *Could you have found which amounts were equivalent without making the model? How?* These questions prompt students to make the link between the forms without using the model as a bridge. Allow a few minutes for partners to reason together and share ideas.

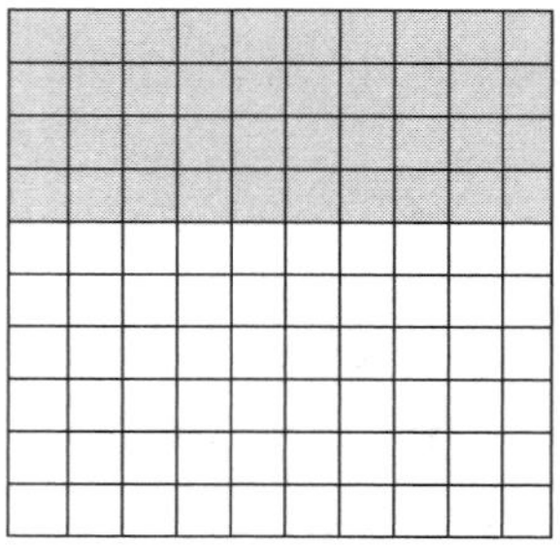

40% colored

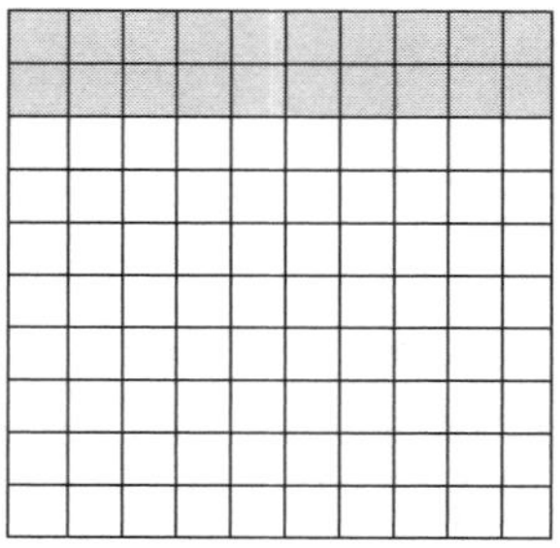

0.20 colored

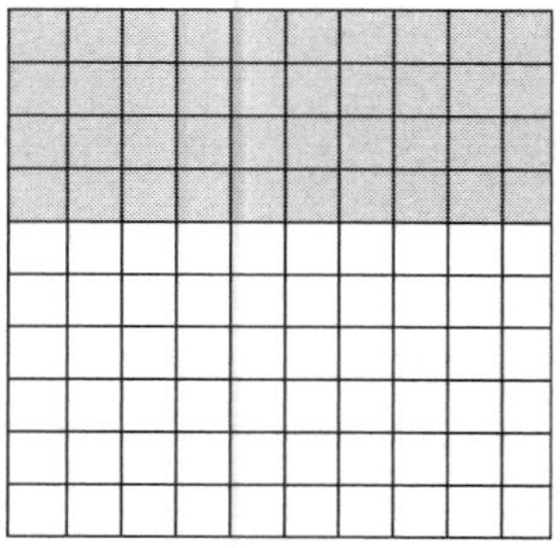

$\frac{2}{5}$ colored

What Might Happen . . . What to Do

Students may have difficulty representing $\frac{2}{5}$ on the hundred grid. Explain that $\frac{2}{5}$ means 2 groups out of 5. Have them show 5 equal groups on the grid and then shade 2 groups. Give students other fractions—such as $\frac{3}{4}$, $\frac{7}{10}$, $\frac{9}{20}$, and so on—to show on their grids.

DISCUSS RESULTS BY POSING QUESTIONS that will focus students' reasoning. *How many equal parts does the grid have?* (One hundred) *What does each square represent?* (One hundredth) *What does percent mean?* ("Per hundred") *When you color in 40% of the grid, how many squares do you color in?* (40) *What other ways can you write 40 hundredths?* (0.40 and $\frac{40}{100}$) *How do you write $\frac{40}{100}$ in lowest terms?* (Divide numerator and denominator by 20; $\frac{2}{5}$.) *What are some other fractions besides $\frac{40}{100}$ and $\frac{2}{5}$ that would be equal to 40%? Explain your thinking.* ($\frac{4}{10}$, $\frac{6}{15}$, $\frac{10}{25}$, and so on) By making these connections, students gain a better understanding of the role 100 plays in converting between forms. The activity also helps students become aware that the same percent has many fractional equivalents.

REVIEW CONVERTING A PERCENT TO A DECIMAL or a fraction. Call on individual students to demonstrate how to convert 50%, 35%, 89%, and 7% to decimals and fractions. If necessary, point out that 7% means 7 out of 100, or $\frac{7}{100}$, and so 7% is 0.07.

Have students use the grids as they develop methods for changing decimals and fractions to percents. Ask them to look at their models for 0.20. *How many of the 100 squares did you color for 0.20?* (20) *What percent is 0.20? Explain.* Then check students' understanding by asking how they would convert 0.3 to a percent. Students should reason that 0.3 is 0.30, which is the same as 30%. Reinforce understanding by asking *If you colored in $\frac{1}{4}$ of the grid, how many squares would you color?* (25) *How could you write $\frac{1}{4}$ with a denominator of 100?* (Multiply numerator and denominator by 25 to get $\frac{25}{100}$.) *What decimal and what percent are the same as $\frac{1}{4}$?* (0.25 and 25%) Communicating these ideas should help students be able to summarize a method for converting fractions to decimals and percents. Connecting different representations of the same amount this way highlights their equivalence. Have students write their steps for converting $\frac{7}{20}$, $\frac{9}{10}$, and $\frac{43}{100}$ to each form.

$$\frac{7}{20} \times \frac{5}{5} = \frac{35}{100} = 0.35 = 35\%$$

$$\frac{9}{10} \times \frac{10}{10} = \frac{90}{100} = 0.90 = 90\%$$

$$\frac{43}{100} = 0.43 = 43\%$$

FINALLY, ASK STUDENTS TO NAME SOME FRACTIONS that cannot be renamed as a common fraction with a denominator of 100. Students may suggest $\frac{1}{3}$, $\frac{1}{6}$, $\frac{3}{8}$, and so on. *Do you remember how to change a fraction to a decimal?* (Divide the numerator by the denominator.) Review if needed. *How could knowing how to change a fraction to a decimal help change some these fractions to percents?* Lead students to understand that by dividing 1 by 3 they obtain the repeating decimal 0.33 . . . , which expressed as a percent is $33\frac{1}{3}\%$. Give students additional practice by asking them to convert $\frac{1}{6}$ and $\frac{3}{8}$ to percents using their method. You may wish to let them perform the division on a calculator so they can focus on conversion concepts. By reasoning about percents and making connections to prior knowledge, students can formulate their own conversion methods and gain a better understanding of the process.

Extension

Use the following as an opportunity for problem solving: *A survey of students at a large middle school showed that $\frac{8}{25}$ of the students came to school by bus, 19% rode bicycles, 0.3 walked, $\frac{3}{20}$ came by car, and 0.04 used other transportation. Rank the forms of transportation from greatest to least. Explain your work.*

Student Pages

Students should now be ready to complete exercises similar to those on the reduced student pages.

Assessment

There were opportunities to assess students' understanding of fractions, decimals, and percents as they made their models and responded to questions about converting between forms. Students' fluency with conversion methods could be judged by noting their responses to oral exercises.

NCTM Standards Summary

Connections to real-life situations were used to raise students' awareness of the need for conversion methods. By taking advantage of their prior knowledge about fractions, decimals, and percent, students could direct their thinking toward developing these methods. Students then used reasoning to formulate meaningful conversion methods based on their understanding rather than the mechanical approaches often presented in textbooks. Reasoning and communication also helped students gain more insight into the relationships among the various forms. Visual representation on hundreds grids enhanced their understanding and helped them link the different forms. Grids also provided them with a tool for verifying their work.

Standard 2 **Algebra**

AT THE SIXTH GRADE LEVEL, algebra includes a lot of work with analyzing patterns and sequences, and the basic operations of multiplication and division. Our lessons are derived from these important topics, and include a lesson on recognizing patterns, a lesson in which students solve problems by finding a pattern, a lesson that explores arithmetic sequences, and a lesson on dividing by powers of ten.

Three lessons model how the process standards can be used to teach content. A fourth lesson is a hypothetical textbook lesson that we have revised to be more standards based. These four lessons do not represent the entire curriculum, but rather provide glimpses of how, with a more concentrated effort to incorporate the process standards, better mathematics teaching and learning can be achieved.

One lesson we have chosen is a lesson in which students recognize and extend numerical patterns. Using the process standards of reasoning and proof, representation, and communication, students see patterns represented in different ways. By discussing these, they realize that there are different ways to look at a particular problem. Students analyze the patterns, express rules for them, and predict later terms.

Another lesson we have chosen is one in which students are to solve problems by finding a pattern. Many connections are made to other areas in mathematics as well as everyday experiences through the choices of problem situations. Students use verbal descriptions, tables, graphs, and diagrams to help them recognize the patterns.

A third lesson that we have chosen explores arithmetic sequences. By focusing on the process standards of reasoning and proof, representation, and communication, students use tables and graphs to identify and graph arithmetic sequences. Students will also be able to find a missing term in an arithmetic sequence.

The hypothetical textbook lesson that we have chosen to revise is one on dividing by multiples and powers of ten. Through better incorporation of the process standards of connections, reasoning and proof, and communication, students will better relate multiplication to their understanding and ability to divide, and to check their results. Having students discuss and try to identify patterns will also help them to have more success.

Standard 2 Lessons

Recognizing Patterns

Finding a Pattern

Exploring Arithmetic Sequences

Using Powers of Ten to Divide

Recognizing Patterns

Introduction

Objective → Students will recognize, describe, and extend visual and numeric patterns.

Context → Students have experience identifying and extending simple patterns. By including this lesson early in the year, patterns can become an ongoing focus in the study of whole number and integer operations, geometry, measurement, and other topics.

NCTM Standards Focus

In this standards-based lesson, students will consider the fundamental questions of when a set of numbers or figures form a pattern and then how can the pattern be described. They will examine different representations of the same pattern to identify relationships that exist and will describe the patterns they find orally and in writing.

Reasoning and Proof Students make generalizations about pattern relationships that lead them to formulate definitions of patterns. They use reasoning to analyze patterns so that they can express rules for continuing those patterns. As students focus their thinking on these key concepts, they gain a better understanding of the range and significance of patterns.

Representation Students study and represent patterns with concrete materials, in numeric sequences, tables, and with drawings. By becoming more fluent with different representation methods, students can choose the approach that helps them to identify pattern rules and continue the pattern.

Communication Encouraging students to share their ideas serves two purposes. First, expressing the rules that describe patterns and identifying additional terms helps students clarify their own thinking. Second, comparing descriptions of the same pattern helps students recognize that there are different ways to look at the same problem.

Teaching Plan

Materials → Student pages 48–49; toothpicks

BEGIN THE LESSON BY WRITING the following numbers on the board and asking students to find the next three numbers.

1, 4, 7, 10, __, __, __

Students should recognize that the next three numbers are 13, 16, and 19, since 3 is being added to each successive term. *How did you find the numbers?* Present this list of numbers to the students. *Would you call this a pattern? Why or why not?*

2, 3, 5, 12, 10, 16

Students should explain that the listing does not indicate a pattern; there does not seem to be any rule relating the numbers. *How would you explain what a pattern is to a friend?* Student explanations may vary, but they all should include the idea that a pattern is a regular, repeating design or sequence of shapes or numbers. Summarize this part of the lesson by pointing out that a pattern must have a rule, and being able to identify, describe, and use the rule is the key to working with patterns.

HAVE STUDENTS WORK IN PAIRS. Distribute a generous supply of toothpicks to each pair and ask them to construct an equilateral triangle using three toothpicks. *Now, add to the triangle you just made and create a single figure made up of two triangles.* Allow students to build their own models, then display solutions on the board or overhead. *How many additional toothpicks were needed?* (2) *How many toothpicks are there in the whole figure?* (5) *Why did you need three toothpicks for the first triangle, but only two more to create the second?* (The triangles share a side.)

Instruct students to work together and continue this pattern until they have a total of 10 triangles. Have them record the total number of toothpicks in each completed step as they work up to 10 triangles. *What rule describes the relationship between the number of triangles and the number of toothpicks you used?* (Start with 3 for the first triangle, then add 2 toothpicks for each new triangle.) Encourage students to offer different ways to explain the rule and then compare descriptions for differences and similarities.

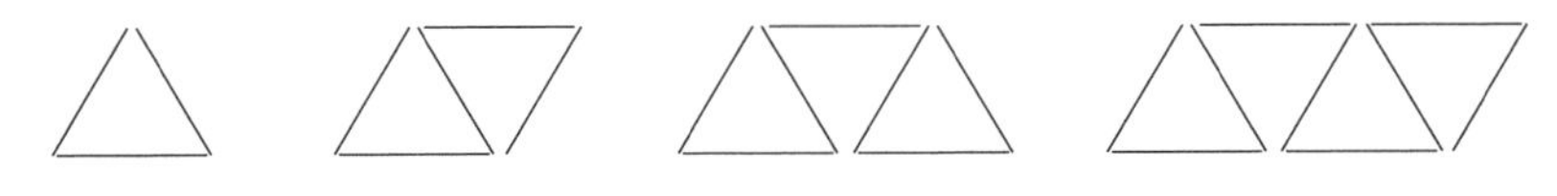

Can you determine the number of toothpicks that would be needed to build 11 and 12 triangles without actually making the model? How? (Continue the pattern; 23 and 25 toothpicks will be used.)

Display a table containing the information gathered about the toothpick pattern for students to examine.

Number of Triangles	1	2	3	4	5	6	7	8	9	10
Number of Toothpicks	3	5	7	9	11	13	15	17	19	21

Remind students that they described the pattern rule above as "start with 3 and add 2 to the previous number of toothpicks to get the next number." *Can you find another way to describe this pattern? Explain.* (Number of toothpicks = 2 (number of triangles) + 1)

Pose questions to help students make distinctions between the two rules. *If you wanted to find the number of toothpicks required for 50 triangles using the first rule we described, what would you need to do? Why?* (You'd have to write out the first 49 numbers in order to have the previous term.) *How could you find the answer using the second rule description?* (Just multiply $2 \times 50 = 100$, then add 1 to get 101.) Help students to understand that the first description involved only the previous number of toothpicks, whereas the second description involved a relationship between the number of triangles *and* the number of toothpicks. Explain that in this example, both descriptions could be found fairly easily, but sometimes only the first type of description will be obvious.

Have students look for another pattern in their toothpick models.

- *When there is one triangle, what is the perimeter of the figure?* (3 units)
- *What is the perimeter of the whole figure when there are two triangles?* (4 units)
- *What is the perimeter of the whole figure when three triangles make up the figure?* (5 units)
- *Do you see a pattern? Explain.* (Each time the number of triangles increases by 1, the perimeter increases by 1.)

Have students continue finding perimeters through 10 triangles and then display the results in a table:

Number of Triangles	1	2	3	4	5	6	7	8	9	10
Perimeter	3	4	5	6	7	8	9	10	11	12

Can you find other ways to describe the pattern? (A possible answer is Perimeter = number of triangles + 2.) *Predict the perimeter for 37 triangles. Explain.* ($37 + 2 = 39$)

FINALLY, MAKE STUDENTS AWARE of the need to have enough terms to clearly characterize a pattern. Ask them to continue the pattern that begins 1, 2, 4, ... Instruct students to write the description or rule for each pattern they create. Have students share their patterns and descriptions with classmates.

Extension

Introduce students to the famous pattern of Fibonacci numbers, 1, 1, 2, 3, 5, 8, 13, 21, 34, 55, . . . , discovered by the Italian mathematician Leonardo Fibonacci. In this pattern, each number after the first is the sum of the previous two numbers. Have students study the pattern and determine the next five numbers. (89, 144, 233, 377, 610)

Assessment

As students extended patterns and explained pattern rules there were opportunities to assess their ability to analyze numerical relationships. You observed whether students could provide multiple descriptions of the same pattern. Student-created patterns, both during the lesson and on completed student pages, also served as indicators of student understanding.

Student Pages

Student page 48 provides students with practice analyzing patterns by examining model drawings and tables. On student page 49, pattern exercises involving numeric and visual relationships lead students to create and describe their own patterns.

NCTM Standards Summary

Students examined patterns and created a meaningful definition of a pattern as a set of numbers or figures that can be described by a rule. Determining the rules for different patterns required students to use reasoning and verify that their rule did, in fact, produce the correct terms. Using different representations of patterns, including models and tables, helped students to analyze patterns in several ways. Throughout this lesson, students communicated their understanding of pattern relationships both orally and in writing. This provided an opportunity to listen to various ways of viewing the same pattern and reinforced students' appreciation of multiple problem-solving strategies.

Answers

Page 48

1. 16 blocks; figure should have 4 arrows on each side
2. Days 16, 23; blocks 16, 20, 32, 56; Answers will vary.
3. A = 13 sq. units; The figure should be a row of 7 squares intersecting a column of 7 squares.
4. Figure 12; areas 17, 25, 37; Answers will vary.

Page 49

1. Upper right square should be shaded
2. A circle divided into fifths
3. Third square should be repeated and should have lower right square subdivided into fourths with the upper left square shaded.
4. $\frac{1}{9}$; $\frac{1}{11}$
5. 0.00005; 0.000006
6. 47; 42
7. Answers will vary.
8. Answers will vary.

Name

Recognizing Patterns

Answer the questions.

❶ The following pattern shows the number of blocks Richard jogs each day with his new exercise program. Draw the figure for Day 4 and write the number of blocks Richard will jog.

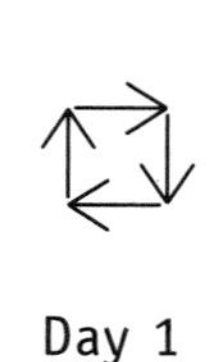

Day 1
4 blocks

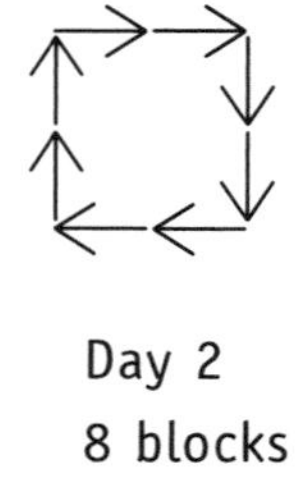

Day 2
8 blocks

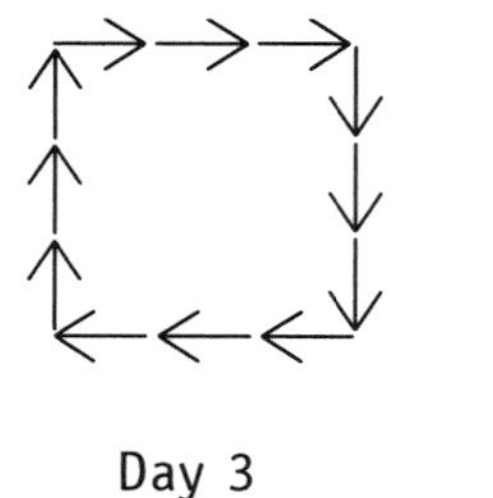

Day 3
12 blocks

____

Day 4

❷ Complete the table.

Day	1	2	3	4	5	8	14		
Number of Blocks	4	8	12					64	92

Explain the pattern rule you used. Then tell how you determined the day when you knew the number of blocks.

❸ In the following pattern, the length of the sides of each square is 1 unit. Draw Figure 4 and write the area.

Figure 1
$A = 1$ sq. unit

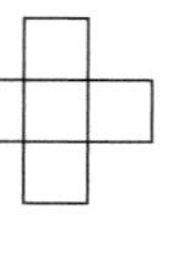

Figure 2
$A = 5$ sq. units

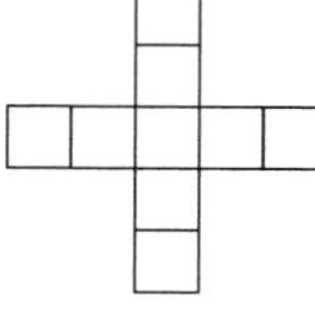

Figure 3
$A = 9$ sq. units

____

Figure 4

❹ Complete the table.

Figure	1	2	3	4	5	7	10	
Area (Square Units)	1	5	9	13				45

Explain the pattern rule you used. Then tell how you found the figure number when you knew the area.

Name ______________________

Recognizing Patterns

Draw the next figure in the pattern.

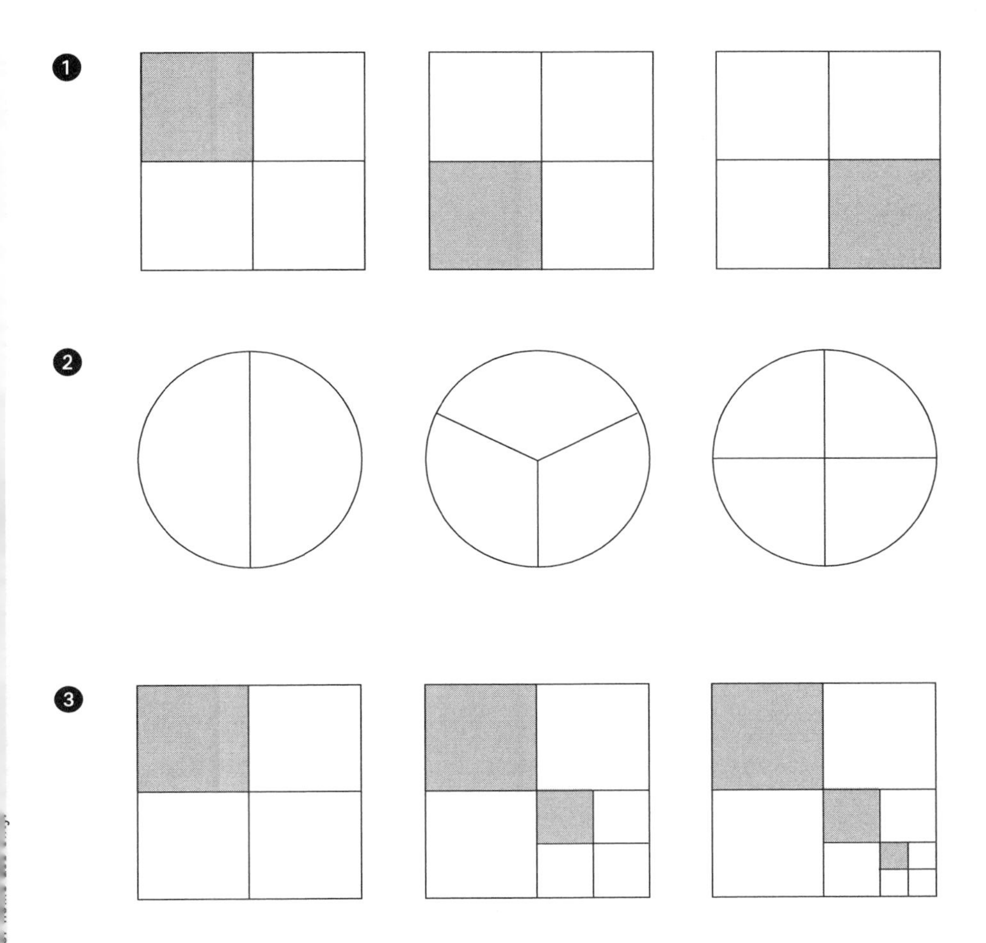

Write the next two numbers in each pattern.

❹ 1, $\frac{1}{3}$, $\frac{1}{5}$, $\frac{1}{7}$, ___, ___

❺ 0.1, 0.02, 0.003, 0.0004, ____, ____, ____

❻ 57, 56, 54, 51, ___, ___

❼ Create a pattern using shapes. Describe your pattern. See if a classmate can figure out your pattern and draw the next two shapes.

❽ Create a pattern using numbers. Describe your pattern. See if a classmate can figure out your pattern and write the next two numbers.

Finding a Pattern

Introduction

Objective → Students will solve mathematical and applied problems by finding a pattern.

Context → This lesson comes early in a unit on patterns and number theory that prepares students for work with fractions. Students have worked with whole-number, integer, and decimal patterns, and they have some experience writing the rule for a pattern and doing coordinate graphing. Students will continue learning algebraic techniques and go on to solve equations.

NCTM Standards Focus

Observing patterns and identifying the rules that apply to those patterns is a powerful problem-solving strategy. With this standards-based approach, rather than being given a strategy to follow, students use their knowledge of number operations and develop their own strategies to define and use patterns they find in solving problems.

Problem Solving In this lesson, students focus on finding patterns to solve real-world problems. Presenting students with a variety of situations helps them recognize different ways that patterns can be involved and helps them see how to identify and use a pattern to find a problem.

Representation Students explore different ways of representing a pattern, including verbal descriptions, tables, graphs, and diagrams. They discover that one representation may be more useful in a particular problem situation and they develop insight into choosing the most helpful method.

Connections Students make connections to whole- and decimal-number operations and geometric concepts to continue patterns. The context of the problems highlight connections to real-world situations, making the lesson more interesting and meaningful for students.

Teaching Plan

Materials → Student pages 54–55; graph paper

BEGIN THE LESSON BY PRESENTING the following situation to the students:

> **The Huntington Middle School has established a banking system that will allow students to use a school credit card for all purchases—lunch, supplies, etc.**

Display the following table. It represents the sign Huntington School posted to explain the fees that would be charged for using the card.

Huntington School Credit Card

Number of Uses Per Month	0	1	2	3	4	5*
Monthly Fee	$1.00	$1.05	$1.10	$1.15	$1.20	$1.25

*Additional usage will be charged using the same rule.

Instruct students to work in pairs and allow time for them to answer questions about the charges posted. *What is the monthly fee just for having the card? How do you know?* ($1.00; If you use the card 0 times, you must pay $1.00.) *How much is the fee charged each time the card is used? How do you know?* (The fee is 5¢ for each use; the monthly fee increases by 5¢ each time the number of uses increases by 1.) *How could you find the monthly fee if you used the card 10 times? 20 times? What are the fees?*

HAVE STUDENTS COMPARE the methods they used to find their answers. Some students will continue the table, adding 5¢ until they reach 10 uses ($1.50) and then 20 uses ($2.00). Other students may find a shorter way, observing that they can multiply the number of uses by 5¢ and add the result to the initial fee of $1.00. Challenge students to write a rule for the pattern based on this method. ($C = \$1.00 + 0.05N$, where N represents the number of uses.) *How would you use this rule to find the fee for 13 uses?* (Substitute 13 for N and carry out the multiplication and addition.)

If no student has suggested graphing as a solution method, present it for consideration. *How would you create a graph of this pattern?* (Use the ordered pairs in the table (0, 1.00), (1, 1.05), and so on.) Have students work with their partners to draw the graph. When students complete their work, ask them to describe the resulting graph. (A set of points that appear to lie along a line.) *How would you use the graph to find the cost for 10 uses?* (Continue the linear pattern of points or draw and extend the line, and then find the vertical coordinate that corresponds to the horizontal coordinate 10.)

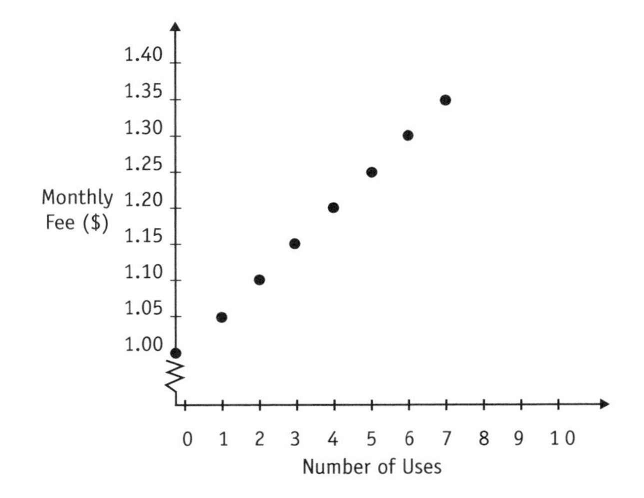

SUMMARIZE BY ASKING STUDENTS to name the three different ways the pattern was represented (Table, algebraic rule or formula, graph). *Which method did you find most convenient for solving problems? Why?*

Next, engage students in thinking about another problem.

> **Suzy Saver and Steven Spender each have $40. By babysitting, Suzy manages to earn enough money to double her total amount each month for 3 months. Steven spends half of what he has each month for 3 months. At the end of the 3 months, how much more money does Suzy have than Steven?**

Allow students time to work; then discuss their solution methods. *How many patterns did you use in this problem?* (Two) *What solution method did you think was best to represent this problem?* (Most students will use tables.) *What numbers did you find for Suzy's pattern?* (40, 80, 160, 320). *For Steven's pattern?* (40, 20, 10, 5). *What is the answer?* (Suzy will have $315 more.)

Motivate students' interest by having them make connections to patterns that can be found in nature and in things people make and do. Encourage students to suggest other patterns that may occur in real-world settings, reminding them that patterns can be geometric—such as in quilts or floor tiles—as well as numeric. Create a list on the board.

CONCLUDE THE LESSON by having students work in pairs to make up two problems of their own involving patterns. You may leave the activity completely open-ended, or you might to choose to offer guidelines. As time allows, have groups share their problems with the class so that all students may gain experience with a broad range of pattern situations.

Extension

Have students use patterns to make up a secret code. Tell them to change each letter of the alphabet using the same rule, make a chart showing the correspondence, and then encode a message to a friend. For example, if each letter in the alphabet were moved ahead by 3 letters, A would be represented by D, B by E, C by F, and so on. The word TODAY would be spelled WRGDB.

Student Pages

Student page 54 offers exercises in pattern identification and representation. Student page 55 provides a variety of problems for students to solve and explain their thinking.

Assessment

Student responses during the class discussion demonstrated their ability to identify and apply patterns in problem-solving situations. As students completed tables, wrote rules, and drew graphs, their fluency with different modes of pattern representation could be assessed.

NCTM Standards Summary

The emphasis of this lesson was on using patterns to solve real-world problems. The discussion helped students to recognize that identifying patterns and pattern rules provides a powerful strategy in problem solving. Having students use multiple representations of the same pattern illustrated connections among verbal, symbolic, and graphic techniques and offered them the option of choosing a method they found to be most convenient. This approach reinforces the concept that there is usually more than one way to solve a problem. Connecting patterns to the real world enhanced the relevance and interest level of this lesson. Students also made connections to prior knowledge as they identified and continued patterns. These opportunities showed how basic operations and number sense are the fundamentals that support continued learning.

Answers

Page 54

1. 11, 13, 15 (add 2)
2. 3.4, 3.9, 4.4 (add 0.5)
3. 16, 32, 64 (double the term)
4. 5, 2.5, 1.25 (divide by 2)
5. 24, 21, 18 (subtract 3)
6. 16, 22, 29 (add number of term to the term)
7. 34, 46, 60 (double the number of the term and add to the term)
8. P, V, C (next letter, skip 1, skip 2, skip 3, and so on)
9. \$18.00, \$21.00; cost equals \$3.00 multiplied by the number of tickets. $c = 3n$
10. 150 mi, 175 mi; total miles equals 25 multiplied by hours driven. $m = 25h$
11. \$14.00, \$20.00; cost equals \$4 plus \$2.00 times the number of rides. $c = \$4 + 2r$
12. 2 yd, $3\frac{1}{3}$ yd; yards equal $\frac{1}{3}$ the number of feet. $y = \frac{1}{3}f$

Page 55

1. 9 rosebushes; 5 years
2. The eleventh stripe would be green; 14 blue, 13 green, 13 yellow stripes; each complete pattern is a multiple of 3 and $3 \times 13 = 39$, so the next color is blue.
3. 9 members by end of March; 81 members by the end of May
4. The letter J is in the 86th square. He completes his name every 5th letter; 86 is one more than 85.
5. 350 cars; 2:30 p.m.

Name ______________________

Finding a Pattern

Complete each pattern.

1. 3, 5, 7, 9, ___, ___, ___
2. 1.4, 1.9, 2.4, 2.9, ___, ___, ___
3. 1, 2, 4, 8, ___, ___, ___
4. 80, 40, 20, 10, ___, ___, ___
5. 36, 33, 30, 27, ___, ___, ___
6. 1, 2, 4, 7, 11, ___, ___, ___
7. 4, 6, 10, 16, 24, ___, ___, ___
8. A, B, D, G, K, ___, ___, ___

Explain the pattern in each table. Write a rule for the pattern. Complete the table.

9.

Number of tickets	1	2	3	4	5	6	7
Total Cost	$3	$6	$9	$12	$15		

10.

Hours	1	2	3	4	5	6	7
Miles Driven	25	50	75	100	125		

11.

Number of rides	0	1	2	3	4	5	8
Admission Charge	$4	$6	$8	$10	$12		

12.

Feet	1	2	3	4	5	6	10
Yards	$\frac{1}{3}$	$\frac{2}{3}$	1	$1\frac{1}{3}$	$1\frac{2}{3}$		

Name

Finding a Pattern

Solve each problem.

1. Lauren began her garden with 3 rosebushes. She plans to plant 2 new bushes every year. How many rosebushes will she have in the third year after she started her garden?

   How many years will it take until her garden has more than 12 rosebushes?

2. Lee is wearing a striped tie. The first stripe is blue, the second stripe is green, and the third is yellow. Then the pattern repeats. What color is the eleventh stripe?

   If the tie has a total of 40 stripes, how many of each color are there? How do you know?

3. Alicia started a volunteer group to help keep parks clean. In January, she was the only member. In February, she found 2 new members. In March, each group member found 2 new members. How many members did the group have at the end of March?

   If the pattern continues, with each member finding 2 new members each month, how many members will the group have at the end of May? How did you find your answer?

4. Jason filled a row of 100 grid squares by writing his name over and over. What letter did he write in the 86th square? Explain how you found your answer.

5. The table shows the number of cars in a mall parking lot at different times.

Time	9:00 a.m.	9:30 a.m.	10:00 a.m.	10:30 a.m.
Number of Cars	50	100	150	200

If the pattern continues, how many cars will be in the lot at noon? When will there be 600 cars in the lot?

Exploring Arithmetic Sequences

Introduction

Objective → Students will identify arithmetic sequences. They will find missing terms in arithmetic sequences and graph the resulting patterns.

Context → Prior to this lesson, students have had experience describing and continuing various patterns involving whole numbers, decimals, integers, and shapes. They are also familiar with coordinate graphing. They will go on to learn about geometric (common ratio) patterns and other principles of number theory.

NCTM Standards Focus

In this lesson, students explore real-life situations to identify patterns, then determine whether those patterns constitute arithmetic sequences. By representing the relationships found in tables, graphs, and finally algebraic notation, students affirm and expand their understanding of the relationships involved and are able to discern the advantages each form of representation offers. Discussing the various methods used in solving for missing terms in the sequences, then using alternative approaches to verify their results, allows students to select a method that is comfortable for them to use and strengthens their problem-solving abilities.

Reasoning and Proof Students discover defining characteristics of arithmetic sequences by comparing and contrasting various sets of numbers. They use reasoning to find missing terms in arithmetic sequences, and by justifying their generalizations, gain insight into the patterns created.

Representation Students represent arithmetic sequences in tables, algebraically, and with graphs. Using multiple representations helps affirm understanding of the relationships formed and provides students with alternate methods for solving problems.

Communication As students describe sequences verbally, they gain experience with recursive definitions. By sharing their ideas, students experience the key features of arithmetic sequences and reinforce their understanding of how to solve problems involving the patterns formed.

Teaching Plan

Materials → Student pages 60–61; graph paper

BEGIN THE LESSON by presenting a situation to engage students in working with arithmetic sequences.

> **Two radio stations are having listener call-in contests. Each contest begins with a certain amount of prize money, and one caller per hour gets the opportunity to win the money by correctly answering a music question. If the caller does not answer correctly, money is added for the next hour. The tables show the amount of prize money that will be available to the next caller after each incorrect answer.**

Radio Station WTMD

Caller Number	1	2	3	4	5
Prize	$100	$150	$200	$250	$300

Radio Station WCPB

Caller Number	1	2	3	4	5
Prize	$100	$125	$175	$250	$350

Suppose you were the seventh caller to WTMD and you answered correctly. How much money would you win? Explain how you know. ($400; $50 is added to the previous amount for each incorrect answer.) *As the seventh caller answering correctly on WCPB, how much would you win? Explain.* ($625; The amount added increases by $25 for each caller.)

How are the sequences of money formed for WTMD and WCPB the same? (Both start with $100; both are increasing patterns.) *How are the sequences different?* (The amount added for WTMD is the same each time; the amount added for WCPB is different each time.)

EXPLAIN THAT THE TABLE for WTMD demonstrates a pattern called an *arithmetic sequence*, which is formed by adding or subtracting the same number repeatedly. Have students examine the following series of numbers and identify whether or not they are arithmetic sequences, and explain why.

2, 9, 16, 23, 30, . . . (Yes; 7 is added each time.)

4, 5, 7, 10, 14, . . . (No; the number added increases by 1 each time.)

2, 4, 8, 16, 32, . . . (No; the pattern involves multiplication.)

80, 70, 60, 50, 40, . . . (Yes; 10 is subtracted each time.)

Prompt students to consider how arithmetic sequences could be represented graphically. *How can we show the information in the table for WTMD with a graph?* (Show number of callers on the horizontal axis and money on the vertical axis.) *What do you think the graph will look like? Why?* (Answers will vary. Some students may visualize a set of points that are along a line.)

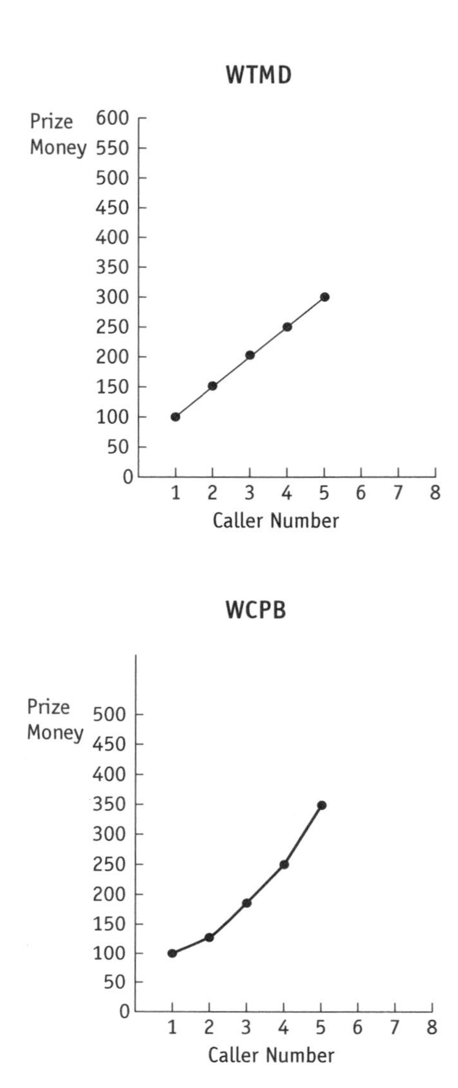

Have students work in pairs to draw a graph of the information for WTMD. Suggest that they try to continue the visual pattern to show other ordered pairs that belong to the sequence. You may also wish to have students draw the graph for WCPB for comparison.

Allow time for students to complete their graphs, then discuss the results. Focus on the graph for WTMD. Point out that the graph of the pattern of any arithmetic sequence will be points lying along a straight line.

Encourage students to develop a formula that expresses the WTMD prize money for any caller by using the beginning amount and the common amount that is being added. Display the following table.

Caller Number	1	2	3	4	5
Amount Added To $100	0(50) = $0	1(50) = $50	2(50) = $100	3(50) = $150	4(50) = $200
Total Prize	$100	$150	$200	$250	$300

What do you notice about the number of times $50 is multiplied to get each prize? (It is one less than the number of callers.) *If* n *represents the number of callers, what is a formula for the prize money?* ($100 + (n - 1)\ 50$) Use this formula to find the prize money for the tenth caller. ($100 + 9(50) = 100 + 450 = 550$. The prize is $550.) *How can you check this answer?* (Find the amount by continuing the pattern.)

Summarize this part of the lesson by explaining that for any arithmetic sequence, the nth number or term of the pattern can be expressed as *nth term* $= a + (n - 1)d$. In this sentence, n represents the number of the term in the sequence, a represents the first term in the sequence, and d is the common amount that is added or subtracted. Reinforce this formula by reviewing the terms and working through an example with the students.

FINALLY, ASK STUDENTSto use what they know about arithmetic sequences to solve the following problem:

The first and fourth numbers in an arithmetic sequence are 7 and 25. Find the rule for this sequence. Find the second and third terms in the sequence.

Pose questions to help students as they think through the process. *Will the rule involve addition or subtraction? How do you know?* (25 is greater than 7, and so the rule must be to add.) *What is the total amount added to 7?* (18) *How many times has the same number been added to 7 to get 25?* (3) *What number is being added each time?* (6) *What are the missing second and third numbers?* (13, 19)

If time allows, have students work in pairs to write one or two problems involving arithmetic sequences. Then have them trade with other students to find the rules and solve the problems.

Student Pages

Page 60 provides practice in identifying arithmetic sequences, writing rules and formulas, and finding missing terms in the sequence. Page 61 allows students to apply their knowledge of arithmetic sequences to solve problems involving real-world settings.

Assessment

As students responded to questions, continued patterns, created graphs, wrote formulas, and found missing terms during the lesson, you could assess their understanding of arithmetic sequences. Student-created problems, as well as their work on the exercises on the student pages, also provided opportunities to evaluate students' fluency with the concepts.

NCTM Standards Summary

Representation was emphasized in this lesson as students used tables, graphs, and algebraic symbolism to express arithmetic sequences. This approach helped students to understand how mathematics provides several methods for working with the same relationship. By applying their own reasoning processes to the representations, students developed the important ideas for themselves. Throughout the lesson, students discussed their work, clarifying ideas for themselves and their audience of peers.

Answers

Page 60

1. Yes; add 4 each time
2. Yes; subtract 8 each time
3. No; multiply by 3
4. Yes; add 0.2 each time
5. No; add 3, then 4, then 5, . . .
6. Add 8; 27, 35, 43
7. Subtract 3; 36, 33, 30
8. Add 2; 8.3, 10.3, 12.3
9. Subtract 0.25; 4.25, 4, 3.75
10. Add 1.4; 36.2, 37.6, 39.0.
11. 3; nth term $= 3 + (n - 1)3$; 10th term $= 30$
12. 2; nth term $= 2 + (n - 1)5$; 10th term $= 47$
13. 15, 24
14. 19, 30
15. 37, 32

Page 61

1. Yes; the rule is add 4.
2. 24, 28, 32
3. nth perimeter $= 4 + (n - 1)4$
4. 15th perimeter $= 4 + 14(4) = 60$
5. nth perimeter $= 4n = 4 + (n - 1)4 = 4 + 4n - 4 = 4n$
6. Answers will vary.
7. 44 wpm; 12th day
8. 7; 25, 32, 39

Name

Exploring Arithmetic Sequences

Is the pattern an arithmetic sequence? Write *yes* or *no*. Explain.

1. 0, 4, 8, 12, . . .

2. 100, 92, 84, 76, . . .

3. 1, 3, 9, 27, . . .

4. 2.8, 3.0, 3.2, 3.4, . . .

5. 3, 6, 10, 15, . . .

The first three terms of an arithmetic sequence are given.
For each sequence, describe the rule and write the next three terms.

6. 3, 11, 19, . . .

7. 45, 42, 39, . . .

8. 2.3, 4.3, 6.3, . . .

9. 5, 4.75, 4.50, . . .

10. 32, 33.4, 34.8, . . .

For each arithmetic sequence given below, (a) identify the first term; (b) write a formula for the *n*th term; (c) use the formula to find the tenth term in each sequence; (d) check your answer.

11. 3, 6, 9, . . .

12. 2, 7, 12, . . .

Find the second and third terms of the arithmetic sequence if

13. the first number is 6 and the fourth number is 33.

14. the first number is 8 and the fourth number is 41.

15. the first number is 42 and the fourth number is 27.

Name ______________________________

Exploring Arithmetic Sequences

The table shows the length of a side of a square garden and the perimeter of the garden.

Length of Side	1	2	3	4	5
Perimeter	4	8	12	16	20

1. Do the numbers in the perimeter row form an arithmetic sequence? Explain.

2. What would be the next three numbers in the perimeter row?

3. Write a formula for the perimeter of a square of side *n* (the nth perimeter) using the first number (perimeter) in the pattern.

4. Use your formula to find the 15th perimeter in the pattern.

5. Do you know another formula for the perimeter of a square of side *n*? Write this formula. Explain why this formula and the one you wrote above give the same perimeters for any value of *n*. (Hint: Use the distributive property.)

6. Draw a graph showing the relationship between the length of the side of a square and its perimeter. Describe your graph.

Solve each problem.

7. Laurie typed 24 words per minute the first day she practiced, 28 words per minute the second day, and 32 words per minute the third day. If the pattern continues, what will Laurie's typing speed be on the sixth day? On which day will Laurie's typing speed be greater than 65 words per minute?

8. Roberto began his collection of trading cards with 18 cards that were a present from his grandfather. Each week, he added the same number of cards to his collection. At the end of five weeks, he had 46 cards. How many cards did Roberto add each week? How many cards did he have at the end of the second, third, and fourth weeks?

Using Powers of Ten to Divide

Introduction

Objective → Students will divide by multiples and powers of 10.

Context → This lesson comes midway in a division unit. Students have reviewed dividing with single-digit divisors and will go on to estimate quotients and divide by two-digit divisors. They understand powers of 10 and have multiplied by powers of 10.

Using Powers of Ten to Divide

Prepare

Multiply: 80×7 80×70 80×700 What pattern do you see?

Learn

Hummingbirds can beat their wings faster than the eye can see.
A hummingbird flaps its wings 9,000 times in 3 minutes.
How many times does it flap its wings in 1 minute?

$$9{,}000 \div 3 = n$$

Use mental math to find the quotient.
Think about a division fact and patterns of tens.

Division fact → $9 \div 3 = 3$

Patterns of 10
$90 \div 3 = 30$
$900 \div 3 = 300$
$9{,}000 \div 3 = 3{,}000$

The pattern shows that the hummingbird flaps its wings 3,000 times every minute.
More examples:

a. $5{,}400 \div 60 = a$

$54 \div 6 = 9$
$540 \div 6 = 90$
$540 \div 60 = 9$
$5{,}400 \div 60 = 90$

b. $40{,}000 \div 500 = b$

$40 \div 5 = 8$
$400 \div 50 = 8$
$4{,}000 \div 500 = 8$
$40{,}000 \div 500 = 80$

Try

Solve. Find n.

1. $480 \div 6 = n$
2. $4{,}500 \div 50 = n$
3. $30{,}000 \div 600 = n$
4. $3{,}500 \div 7 = n$
5. $n = 42{,}000 \div 600$
6. $7{,}200 \div 90 = n$

Show the division fact and the pattern of tens used to find $64{,}000 \div 80 = 800$.

NCTM Process Standards Analysis and Focus

The standards analysis examines how the process standards have been incorporated into the above lesson. By increasing the focus on three of the process standards, a more effective and meaningful lesson can be presented. The suggestions offered can help you to think about how this might be accomplished.

Connections The lesson shows an interesting method of division; however, the connection between multiplication and division that facilitates dividing by powers of 10 is missing.

Suggestion → **Invoke prior knowledge of basic multiplication and division facts. Thinking about multiplication to determine a quotient will focus on the relationship between divisor and dividend and help students solve division**

Practice

Use mental math. Solve.

7. $600 \div 30 = n$
8. $4{,}000 \div 500 = n$
9. $4{,}200 \div 600 = n$
10. $490{,}000 \div 700 = n$
11. $320 \div 80 = n$
12. $15{,}000 \div 300 = n$
13. $2{,}700 \div 9 = n$
14. $640{,}000 \div 8{,}000 = n$
15. $63{,}000 \div 90 = n$
16. $35{,}000 \div a = 50$
17. $240{,}000 \div 800 = c$
18. $100{,}000 \div 250 = y$
19. $b \div 600 = 9{,}000$
20. $42{,}000 \div x = 70$
21. $z \div 8{,}000 = 90$

Problem Solving

Use mental math to solve.

22. A train traveled 720 kilometers. Its average speed was 80 kilometers per hour. How many hours was the train traveling?
23. Louise drove 120 kilometers in 2 hours. Anita drove 210 kilometers in 3 hours. How much faster did Anita drive?
24. A test pilot flew a jet at 1,640 kilometers per hour. The next week, he flew at 1,860 kilometers per hour. How much faster did he fly the second week?
25. A passenger plane flew approximately 2,000 miles from Chicago to San Francisco. The trip took 4 hours. What was the plane's average speed?

History Connection

This is a method of division that was used in the 1960's and 70's.

60)24,360		
6,000	100	Make a guess and multiply.
18,360		Find what is left over.
18,000	300	Guess again.
360		Find what is left over.
360	6	Guess again.
0		Stop when you can't guess any more.
	406	Add your guesses for the answer.

26. Write a problem with a 5-digit dividend and a 2-digit divisor that uses the fact $25 \div 5$.
27. Write a problem with a 6-digit dividend and a 3-digit divisor that uses the fact $18 \div 3$.
28. Write a problem with a 4-digit dividend and a 3-digit division that uses the fact $28 \div 7$.

problems with greater facility. Making connections between horizontal division sentences and the standard long division form will help students gain more insight into the meaning of division.

Reasoning and Proof The lesson offers limited opportunities for reasoning and proof.

Suggestion → **Have students identify patterns related to multiplying by powers of 10 and explain how they can apply those patterns when solving division problems. Using this type of reasoning will help students master the place-value concepts involved in the division process. Encourage students to use their understanding of the relationship between multiplication and division to check their quotients.**

Communication The lesson offers few opportunities for communication.

Suggestion → **Provide opportunities for students to discuss relationships they find between multiplication and division patterns that involve powers of 10. Sharing ideas will enhance awareness of different ways to think about the division process.**

Problem Solving The problem-solving section presents word problems that provide additional division practice, but these exercises do not involve actual problem solving.

Representation Division sentences in which the factors are multiplied by powers of 10 represent variations of basic division facts.

The teaching plan that follows shows how the suggestions for increasing the focus on the process standards can be implemented.

Revised Teaching Plan

BEGIN THE LESSON WITH A BRIEF REVIEW of multiplication patterns using multiples and powers of 10. Start with a basic fact, and then expand on that fact by having students find products when factors are multiplied by 10, 100, 1,000, and 10,000. Emphasize the place-value aspect of the zeros in the products. For example, write the basic fact $3 \times 2 = 6$ on the board, and then show students that $3 \times 20 = 3 \times 2$ tens $= 6$ tens $= 60$. Point out that one zero to the right of the 6 moves the 6 into the tens column. Ask students to supply the similar place-value reasoning for 3×200 and so on. Include other examples such as 4×6, 4×60, and so on for reinforcement.

Present a situation involving division, such as *A company paid* \$480 *for 6 desks. How much did each desk cost?* Write the division equation $480 \div 6 = n$ and the long division form, $6\overline{)480}$ with n above, on the board. Help students make the connection between terms in the two formats. Ask students what n represents in each form. (The quotient) Make the fundamental connection between division and multiplication by reminding students that $480 \div 6 = n$ and $6 \times n = 480$ are related facts. Highlight the corresponding numbers in the sentence and long division forms to connect the divisors, dividends, and quotients. This will help students more clearly understand the algebraic representation.

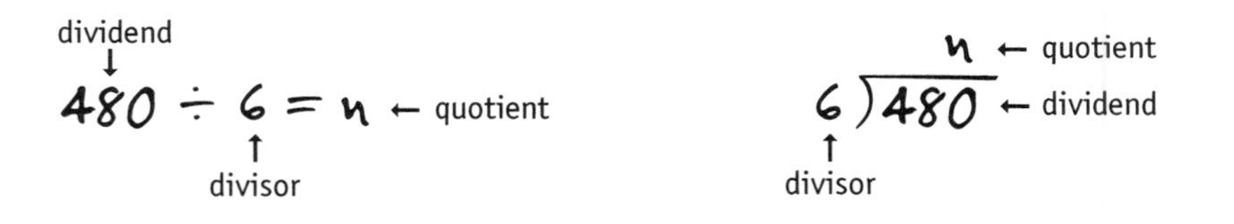

ASK STUDENTS TO DETERMINE THE VALUE of n using a method of their own choosing and to record their work. Have students share their procedures. Some students may have approached the problem by using a multiplication fact while others used a division fact. Be sure to point this out to emphasize the relationship between the operations. Help students find patterns and generalize a process.

What basic multiplication fact is used in this problem? ($6 \times 8 = 48$) *What is the relationship between 48 and 480?* (480 is 48 multiplied by 10.) *Since* 6 *is the divisor, we'll find out how many* 6s *it takes to make* 480. *What number multiplied by 6 is 480? How do you know?* Students should be able to reason that $6 \times 8 = 48$ and $480 = 10 \times 48$. One of the factors in this basic fact must have been multiplied by 10. Since 6 was identified as the divisor, the other factor, 8, must have been multiplied by 10. Therefore, $6 \times 80 = 480$.

Having students first focus on multiplication and then relating multiplication to division extends prior knowledge. It illustrates how different skills that have already been learned combine to solve a broader range of problems. Emphasize that students didn't learn new material in this lesson, but rather they learned to apply information they already knew in a different way.

PRESENT A PROBLEM such as $30{,}000 \div 500 = n$ in which both numbers are multiples of powers of 10. Ask students to write the related multiplication equation $500 \times n = 30{,}000$ and identify the basic fact, $5 \times 6 = 30$, that is the core of this equation. Have students solve the problem and record their work. Then invite students to discuss their methods.

What Might Happen . . . What to Do

In solving an equation such as $30{,}000 \div 500 = n$, students may not understand when to stop working with one factor and focus on the other factor, and they may arrive at an answer like $5{,}000 \times 6 = 30{,}000$. Review the related original division and multiplication sentences explaining how the divisor 500 becomes a factor. Circle the 500. Tell students the circle represents a stop sign; when one factor matches the divisor in that sign, they must stop and adjust the other factor. Have students practice until they understand the method well enough to dispense with the circling.

Have students work in pairs to solve two additional problems. Instruct students to take turns explaining the steps to use and giving reasons for the steps. By talking about and listening to the thinking involved, students will reinforce their understanding of the process. Once again, emphasize the connection between division and multiplication by asking students to verify their answers to division problems using the related multiplication. Have individual students explain their solutions to the class.

Conclude the lesson with a brief summary to help the students organize information about their methods and formulate a procedure to use with division problems like those they have been working on. A simple list of steps reflecting what to do can be recorded on the board.

One Way to Find the Quotient

Step 1 Write the related multiplication equation.

Step 2 Identify and write the basic multiplication fact.

Step 3 Multiply one factor by a power of 10 and find a revised product.

Step 4 Compare the new product and, if necessary, multiply the second factor by a power of 10.

Student Pages

Students should now be ready to complete excercises similar to those on the reduced student pages.Consider asking students to write the multiplication fact for each problem and having them check quotients using multiplication.

Assessment

Reviewing patterns of multiplication with powers of 10 offered an opportunity to assess students' understanding of the role of place value in products. As students explained their thinking and methods for solving division problems, their application of mathematical relationships and processes could be evaluated.

NCTM Standards Summary

Making connections to basic facts and to multiplication patterns made working with division easier. Requiring students to explain their work and prove their results helped them clarify thinking and strengthen understanding. Increased opportunities for communication meant that all students could gain better insight into number patterns and mathematical processes. Making these changes to the lesson placed the focus on the number sense students need to develop to be successful with mental math.

Standard 3 **Geometry**

AT THE SIXTH GRADE LEVEL, geometry includes a lot of work with two- and three-dimensional figures and triangle relationships. Our lessons are derived from these important topics, and include a lesson on exploring cross sections, a lesson on the Pythagorean Theorem, a lesson on possible and impossible figures, and a lesson on classifying triangles.

Three lessons model how the process standards can be used to teach content. A fourth lesson is a hypothetical textbook lesson that we have revised to be more standards based. These four lessons do not represent the entire curriculum, but rather provide glimpses of how, with a more concentrated effort to incorporate the process standards, better mathematics teaching and learning can be achieved.

One lesson we have chosen has students produce and identify different cross sections of solid figures. This lesson is often overlooked or not given much emphasis, but by basing the lesson on the process standards representation, reasoning and proof, and connections, students will improve their visualization skills and spatial sense. Students will also see how knowledge of cross sections can be applied.

Another lesson we have chosen is one that develops the Pythagorean Theorem. The process standards of representation and connections drive this lesson as students model the Pythagorean Theorem geometrically, then make connections to the algebraic representation.

A third lesson we have chosen is one in which students explore whether, given certain specifications, a figure is possible or impossible to draw. The process standards of representation, reasoning and proof, and communication are important here as students are either able to draw a figure or explain why it cannot be drawn. Discussion opportunities give students a chance to reinforce their knowledge of the properties of plane figures.

The hypothetical textbook lesson we have chosen to revise is one that has students classify triangles by the lengths of the sides or by the measures of the angles. Students are usually given definitions, then asked to identify triangles according to those definitions. Through better incorporation of the process standards of reasoning and proof, connections, and communication, students focus on the attributes of the triangles and make distinctions among the different types.

Standard 3 Lessons

Visualizing Cross Sections

Demonstrating the Pythagorean Theorem

Exploring Possible and Impossible Figures

Classifying Triangles

Visualizing Cross Sections

Introduction

Objective → Students will identify and explain how to produce different cross sections of a given solid figure.

Context → This lesson comes early in the study of solid figures in a geometry unit. Students are familiar with plane figures and the names and properties of basic solid figures. They have calculated areas and perimeters and will go on to learn about volume and surface area.

NCTM Standards Focus

Creating and visualizing cross sections of three-dimensional shapes is an important skill that is often neglected in the study of geometry. In this lesson, students have an opportunity to connect their prior knowledge about plane figures with the cross sections that result when a plane cuts geometric shapes. Students consider whether cross sections of a particular figure are constant or variable, and they justify their ideas with models and drawings. These activities help students develop and reinforce their visualization skills. Opportunities for students to apply their understanding of cross sections to real-life situations make the lesson relevant for students.

Representation Students use three-dimensional models to help them visualize two-dimensional cross sections. They visualize the shapes that correspond to given cross sections and make drawings of cross sections to correspond to differently positioned slices. These activities help students improve their visualization skills and develop spatial sense that will be important as they continue to work with solids.

Reasoning and Proof Using their understanding of plane and solid shapes to make logical arguments, students justify their conclusions about cross sections and corresponding figures. They support their thinking with drawings or construct models to demonstrate their ideas. These opportunities for reasoning help students clarify and affirm their thinking about basic geometric relationships.

Connections Students make connections between plane and solid figures. They rely on prior knowledge of plane figures and the concept of symmetry to solve problems. Opportunities for students to connect cross sections to real-life situations give the concepts added meaning.

Teaching Plan

Materials → Student pages 74–75; modeling clay; metal spatulas or rulers; geometric solids or pictures of geometric shapes; mirrors

INTRODUCE THE LESSON by explaining that when a three-dimensional shape is cut by a plane, a new figure is formed. This figure is called a *cross section*. *Will a cross section be a three-dimensional figure like the original shape, or will it be a two-dimensional (plane) figure?* (A two-dimensional, or plane, figure) Encourage students to explain their thinking as they give their responses.

Display a model or drawing of a cube, and lead students through questions to help them visualize the cross sections of this figure. *If you sliced this cube horizontally, what would the cross section look like?* (A square) *Why?* (The cross section will be like a face of the cube, which is a square.) *What if you sliced the cube vertically?* (The cross section would also be a square.) *Would the dimensions of the square change depending on where you made your slice?* (No. All of the cross sections, both horizontal and vertical, would be congruent.)

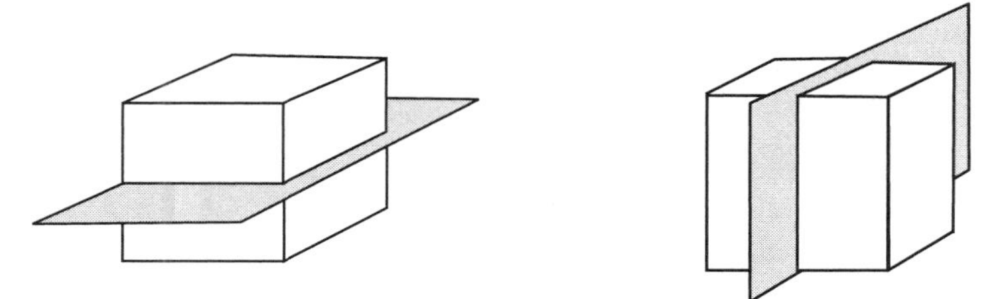

f.y.i.

Many people have difficulty visualizing cross sections that result from cutting through three-dimensional figures. Making clay figures and then cutting through them provides a physical model that can be helpful in building understanding of this concept.

HAVE STUDENTS WORK in pairs or groups of three. Direct them to make a cylinder out of clay. Tell them they are going to explore the cross sections formed when the cylinder is sliced with a spatula or ruler. *What does the spatula (or ruler) you are using represent?* (A plane) Have students slice their cylinder model horizontally, vertically, and tilted at an angle as shown. Instruct students to make a drawing of each cross section and to include a written description of it.

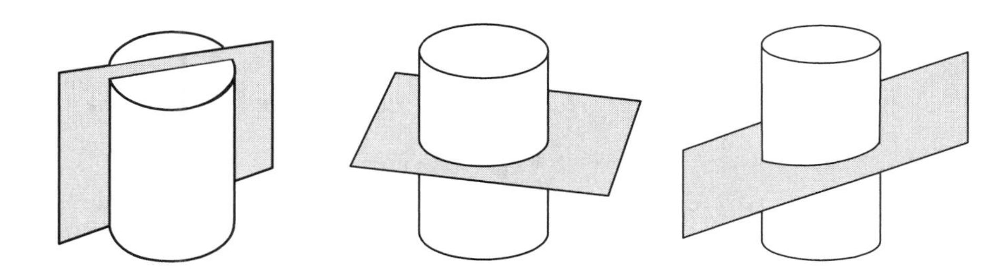

When students are finished, ask them to identify the cross sections they created. They should indicate that the horizontal section is a circle, the vertical section is a rectangle, and the tilted section is an oval, or ellipse. *Will all the circular cross sections be the same size no matter where you make your slice?* (Yes.) *Will all the rectangular sections be the same size no matter where you make your slice?* (No.) *How can you get the largest rectangle?*

(The largest rectangle results from a slice through the center of the cylinder. The rectangles become narrower as you move away from the center of the circle.) *How could you change the shape of the oval cross section?* (By slicing at different angles) Encourage students to verify this information by making additional slices of their cylinders.

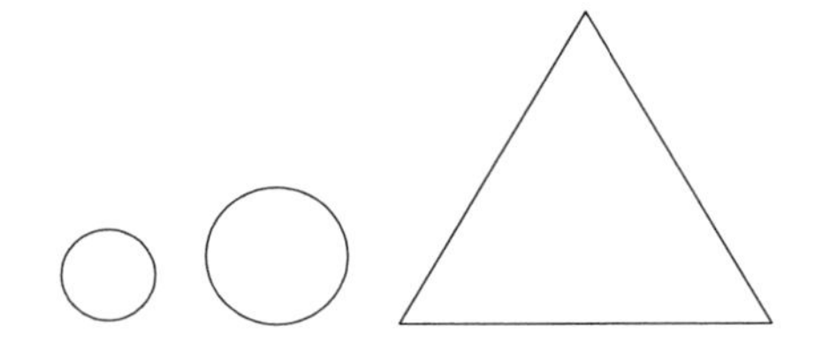

SHOW STUDENTS DRAWINGS of two circles of different sizes and a triangle. Inform students that these shapes are all cross sections of the same figure. Ask students to draw a solid figure that could produce these cross sections when sliced. This will be an opportunity for students to combine their reasoning and visualization skills.

What Might Happen . . . What to Do

Some students might create a model of a pyramid rather than a cone as a match for the triangular shape. Work with them individually to help them see that a horizontal slice of a triangular pyramid will produce a triangle rather than a circle, and a square pyramid will produce a square. Encourage them to make models of clay and cut through them.

Ask students to display and compare their completed drawings. *What figure did you create?* (A cone) *How could you verify that the figure you drew is correct?* (By creating a model and comparing the original three shapes with slices of the model) *Do you think a cone could be sliced to produce an oval cross section and, if so, how?* (Yes. Tilt the slice from the horizontal position.) Encourage students to verify their thinking by having them make slices of a clay model and describe the position of the slice for each cross section they make. Students can also make drawings of the sections they think might result if the cone is sliced vertically along its side.

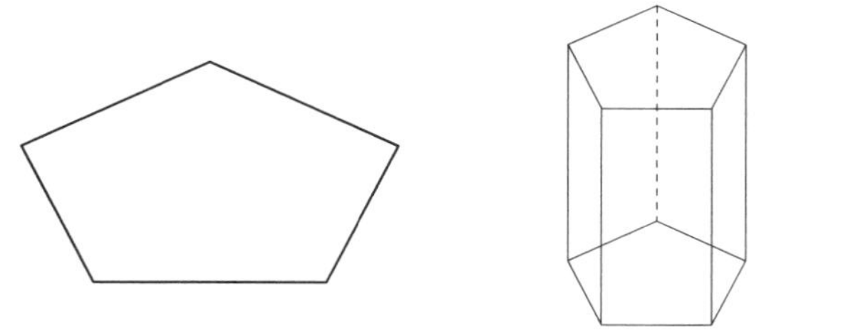

Now ask students to identify possible solids that would produce a horizontal cross section in the shape of a pentagon. (A pentagonal prism or a pentagonal pyramid) Encourage students to try drawing vertical cross sections for these figures. The cross sections will be either rectangles or triangles. Students might again use clay models to verify their conclusions.

As a concluding activity, encourage students to create some combination figures such as a cube topped by a square pyramid, or a cylinder topped by a cone, or some irregular solids, and sketch the different cross sections they think could be obtained. Students can share and discuss their work as a class. To verify their thinking, they can create the shapes in clay and make slices to match those they made in their drawings.

Student Pages

Student page 74 provides additional practice in identifying cross sections. Student page 75 presents real-life situations in which students can apply their visualization skills and understanding of cross sections.

Assessment

Students' drawings and models, and their written and verbal descriptions of cross sections served as indicators of their familiarity with geometric figures and their ability to understand and visualize cross sections that result when a plane cuts through figures. The exercises on the student pages provided additional opportunities to assess students' understanding of cross sections.

NCTM Standards Summary

Representation was an important part of this lesson as students worked with models and connected prior knowledge about plane figures to making cross sections and drawings of cross sections. This approach helped students develop and reinforce their visualization skills as they made connections between two-dimensional and three-dimensional figures. As students focused their thinking on whether cross sections of a particular figure were constant or variable, and then justified their ideas with models and drawings, they enhanced their understanding of the figure's physical form. The student pages presented opportunities for students to apply their understanding of cross sections to real-life situations making the topic more relevant and interesting for students.

Answers

Page 74

1. Circle
2. Rectangle
3. Rectangle
4. Square
5. Triangle

Page 75

1. They are all circles.
2. They are all circles.
3. An infinite number
4. The Equator
5. The square pyramid and the cone—both have triangular cross sections
6. The square pyramid and the cylinder—both have square cross sections
7. The cone and cylinder—both have circular cross sections
8. There are several possibilities. Use the cone in A, the pyramid in B, and the cylinder in C; or use the pyramid in A, the cylinder in B, and the cone in C.

Name ______________________________

Visualizing Cross Sections

Identify the cross section formed in each situation. Name the figure resulting from the cross section and make a drawing.

❶

❷

❸

❹

❺

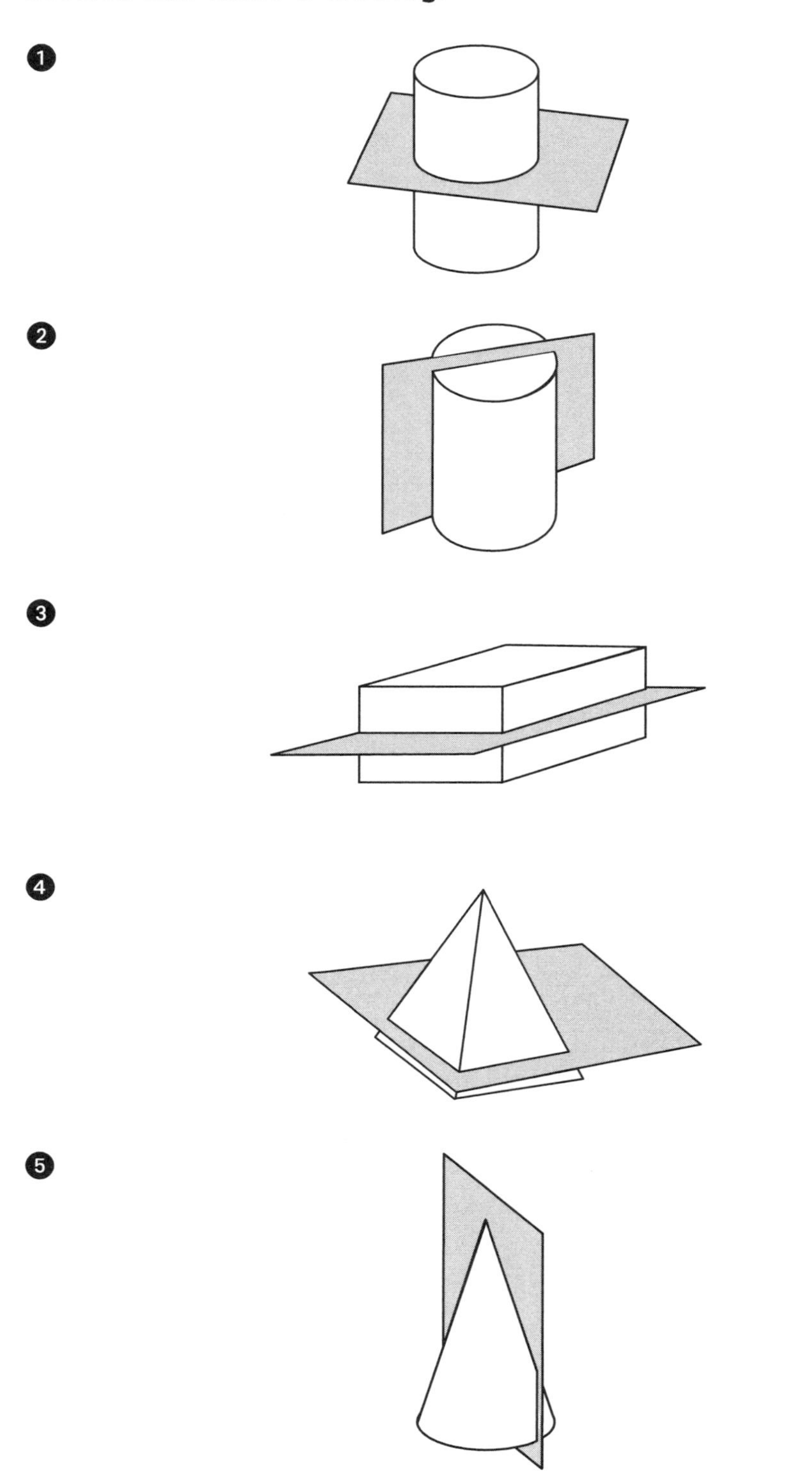

Name

Visualizing Cross Sections

Use the drawings to answer the questions.

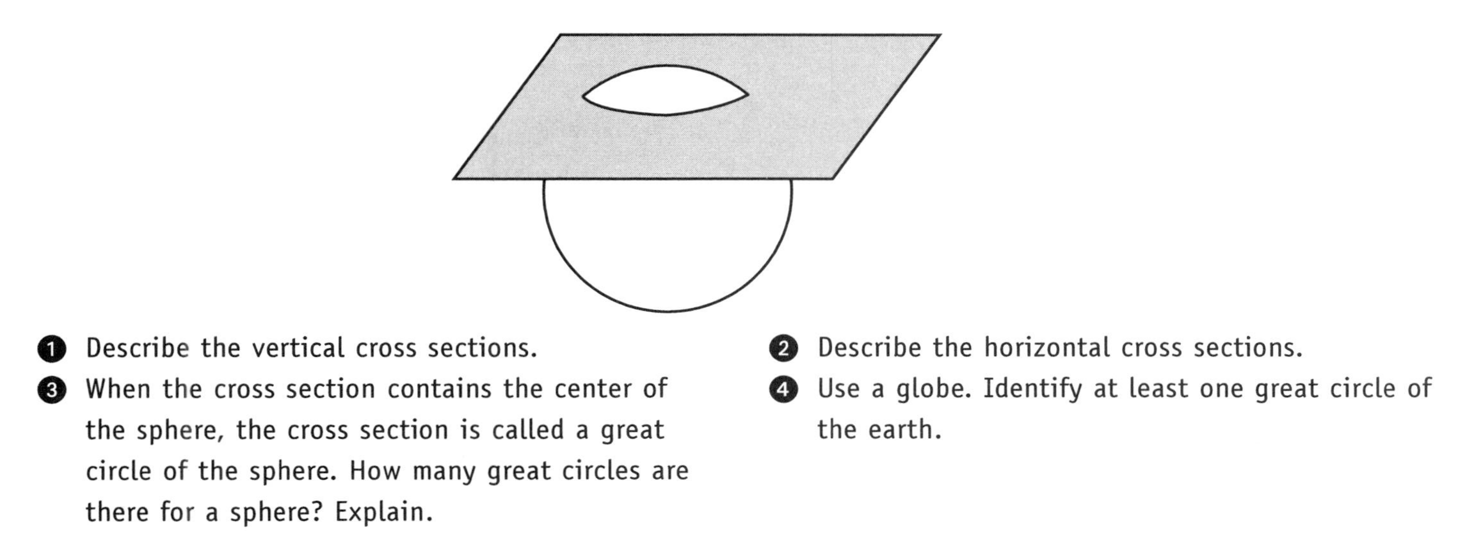

1. Describe the vertical cross sections.
2. Describe the horizontal cross sections.
3. When the cross section contains the center of the sphere, the cross section is called a great circle of the sphere. How many great circles are there for a sphere? Explain.
4. Use a globe. Identify at least one great circle of the earth.

Roger just discovered that his rowboat has three holes and water is leaking in! The holes look like this:

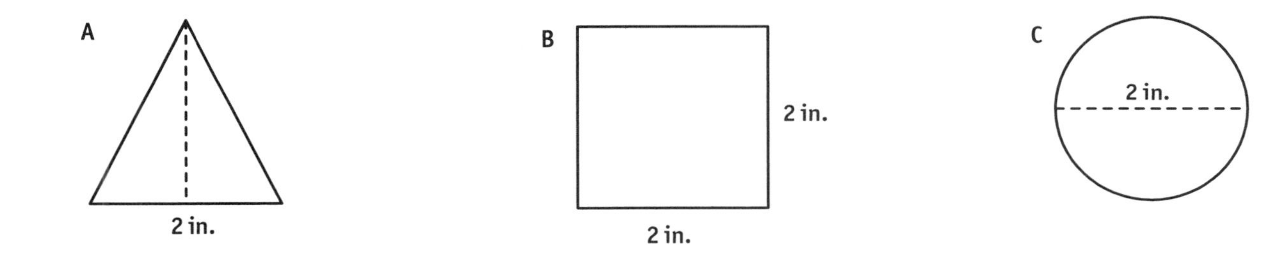

Fortunately, he also has three rubber stoppers with him. The stoppers have these shapes.

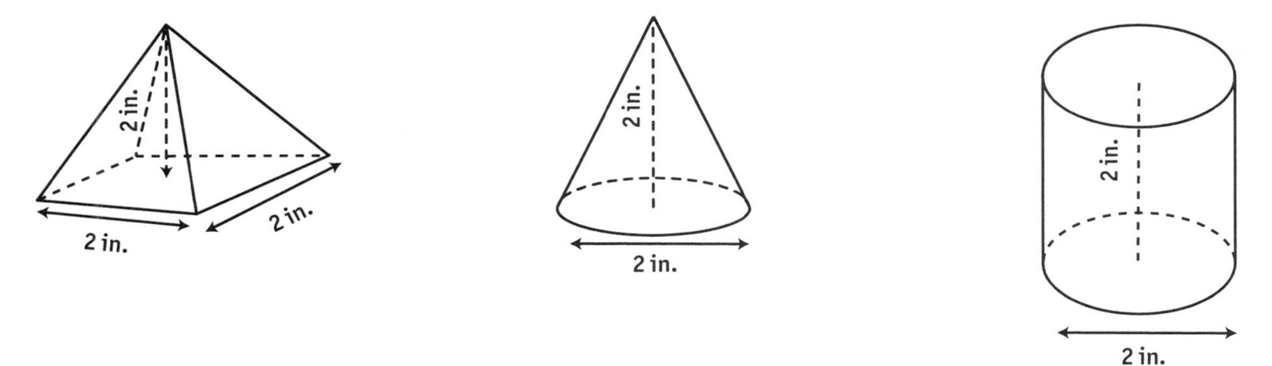

5. Which stopper(s) would fit hole A? Explain.
6. Which stopper(s) would fit hole B? Explain.
7. Which stopper would fit hole C? Explain.
8. Which stopper(s) should Roger use to fix the leaks in his boat? Is there more than one way? Explain.

Demonstrating the Pythagorean Theorem

Introduction

Objective → Students will describe and apply the Pythagorean Theorem which deals with the relationship of the sides of right triangles.

Context → This lesson comes toward the end of a geometry unit in which students have learned about lines, angles, polygons, similarity, and congruence. They are also familiar with finding area of rectangles and squares.

NCTM Standards Focus

Students represent the Pythagorean Theorem geometrically and then connect the geometric model with the familiar algebraic notation, gaining a level of understanding of this important concept that cannot be attained from merely reading about it in a textbook. Students create models of right triangles and build squares along the legs of the triangles. Then they use their knowledge of area to reason through and explain the relationships that exist in the models. Their understanding is reinforced and extended as they make and verify predictions about measurements related to other right triangles.

Representation Students model the Pythagorean relationship. Manipulating areas and examining the model gives meaning to the representation of this relationship in algebraic form.

Reasoning and Proof Students examine a geometric model to discover relationships represented by the Pythagorean Theorem. They express the Pythagorean Theorem in their own words. Doing this affirms their understanding of the theorem and helps them to remember it.

Connections Students employ prior knowledge about exponents, polygons, and area as they explore the Pythagorean Theorem. The connection between the geometric model and the algebraic formula is emphasized, giving students experience with how different areas of mathematics are related.

Teaching Plan

Materials → Student pages 80–81; centimeter graph paper; scissors; tape

BEGIN THE LESSON with a brief review of the properties of right triangles. *What is a right triangle?* (A triangle with one 90°, or right angle) Draw a few right triangles on the board to show different orientations and shapes. Include at least one isosceles right triangle.

Inform students that one of the most famous relationships in mathematics involves the sides of a right triangle. It is named for its discoverer, the Greek mathematician Pythagoras, who lived from 572 B.C. to 501 B.C. Pythagoras founded a society devoted to the study of mathematics, music, and astronomy. Members of the society believed that numerical relationships could be used to describe what happened in the natural world.

Have students work individually or in pairs. Tell them they are to create two right angles with sides of 3 centimeters and 4 centimeters on graph paper. *How do you know you have created a right angle?* (The horizontal and vertical lines of the graph paper intersect at right angles.) Next, direct students to build a 3-by-3 square along the 3-centimeter side and a 4-by-4 square along the 4-centimeter side of one of the right angles they have drawn. Ask students to state the area of each square and explain how they know. Tell students to carefully cut out each of these squares.

Now have them turn the second right angle into a right triangle by drawing the third side. Explain that in a right triangle, the longest side is opposite the right angle and is called the *hypotenuse*. The other sides of the triangle are called *legs*.

CHALLENGE STUDENTS TO THINK about how they can use their cutout squares to determine the length of the hypotenuse. Suggest they consider building a square along the hypotenuse and determining its area to help them answer the question. (If they know the area of a square, they can find the length of a side using the formula $A = s \times s = s^2$.)

Have students use their 9-square and 16-square cutouts to create a square that will fit on the hypotenuse. The square that is created should be 5-by-5.

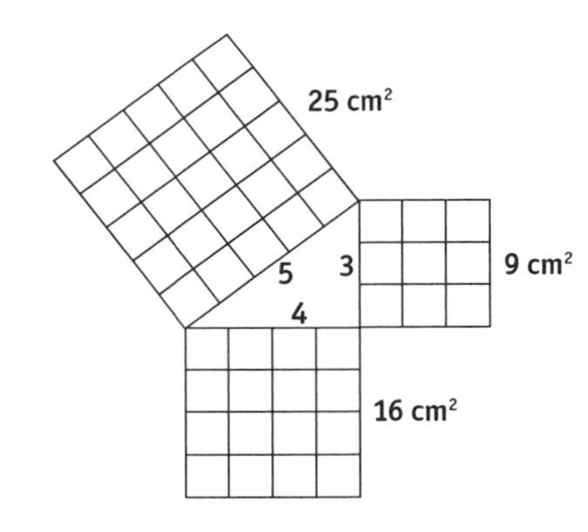

WHEN STUDENTS HAVE COMPLETED their work, ask them to explain what they have demonstrated in their own words. In this way, students will develop the right triangle relationship through their own reasoning process. The result will be more meaningful to them and they will be more likely to remember it. Have them compare their methods and arrangements.

Students should express that the area of the square along the hypotenuse is equal to the sum of the areas of the squares along the other two sides, or legs. *What is the numerical relationship for this right triangle?* ($9 + 16 = 25$, or $3^2 + 4^2 = 5^2$)

Explain to students that Pythagoras is credited with proving that this relationship is true for every right triangle. The Pythagorean Theorem states that if the lengths of the legs of a right triangle are represented as a and b, and the length of the hypotenuse is c, then $a^2 + b^2 = c^2$. Emphasize that it is also true that if the sides of a triangle satisfy the Pythagorean Theorem, then the triangle is a right triangle.

Conclude the lesson by having students create another right triangle with legs having lengths of 6 centimeters and 8 centimeters. Ask them to predict the area of the square formed along the hypotenuse. ($36 + 64 = 100$ square centimeters) *If your prediction is correct, what is the length of the hypotenuse of the triangle? Explain.* (10 cm; $10 \times 10 = 100$) Have students repeat the steps of the activity of cutting out and fitting the squares together to verify their predictions. You might wish to mention that right triangles are often described using the three whole-number measures from the Pythagorean Theorem. These three numbers are referred to as a Pythagorean triples. For example, the first triangle they worked with would be referred to as a 3–4–5 right triangle, and the second, a 6–8–10 triangle.

Extension

An isosceles right triangle has two equal sides. Ask students to explain how the diagram shown here illustrates the Pythagorean Theorem for isosceles right triangles. As a hint, you might tell students it is as easy as $2 + 2$.

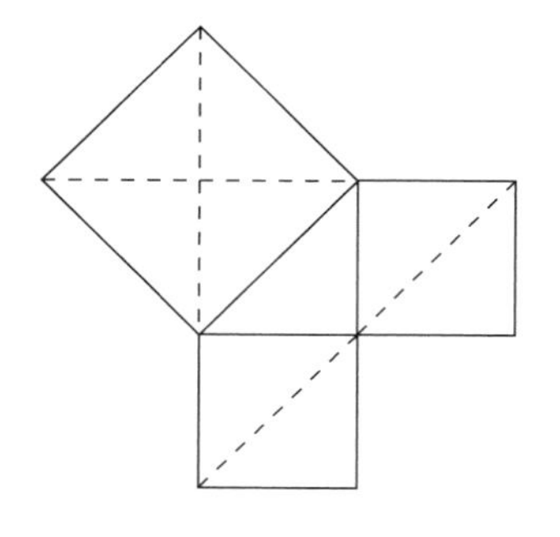

Student Pages

Student page 80 gives students practice in using visual models to write the Pythagorean relationship. Student page 81 provides exercises in which students apply the Pythagorean Theorem to find measures of sides of right angles.

Assessment

Students' success in completing the triangle models and their expression of the Pythagorean relationship served as indicators of their understanding of the lesson. The exercises on the student pages provided additional opportunities to assess students' abilities in applying the Pythagorean Theorem in different ways.

NCTM Standards Summary

Representing the Pythagorean Theorem geometrically allowed students to be actively engaged in learning this important concept. Consequently, the relationships involved were more meaningful and more firmly fixed in students' minds than had they simply been read about on a textbook page. Representation was also important in connecting the geometric relationship and algebraic expression, showing students how different areas of mathematics work together to build new knowledge. Using their own reasoning processes, students expressed their discoveries and then demonstrated their understanding by making and verifying predictions for other right triangles. By helping them to thoroughly understand a fundamental concept, this lesson provided students a foundation for success in later problem-solving situations involving right triangles.

Answers

Page 80

1. $a^2 + b^2 = c^2$;
   $5^2 + 12^2 = 13^2$;
   $25 + 144 = 169$
2. $a^2 + b^2 = c^2$;
   $9^2 + 12^2 = 15^2$;
   $81 + 144 = 225$
3. $a^2 + b^2 = c^2$;
   $8^2 + 15^2 + 17^2$;
   $64 + 225 = 289$

Page 81

1–3. Figures should be properly labeled.
4. 256 cm^2
5. 144 cm^2
6. 400 cm^2
7. 400 cm^2
8. 20 cm
9. Yes
10. No
11. Yes
12. No
13. Yes
14. No

Name

Demonstrating the Pythagorean Theorem

Show that the Pythagorean Theorem works for each triangle. Use $a^2 + b^2 = c^2$.

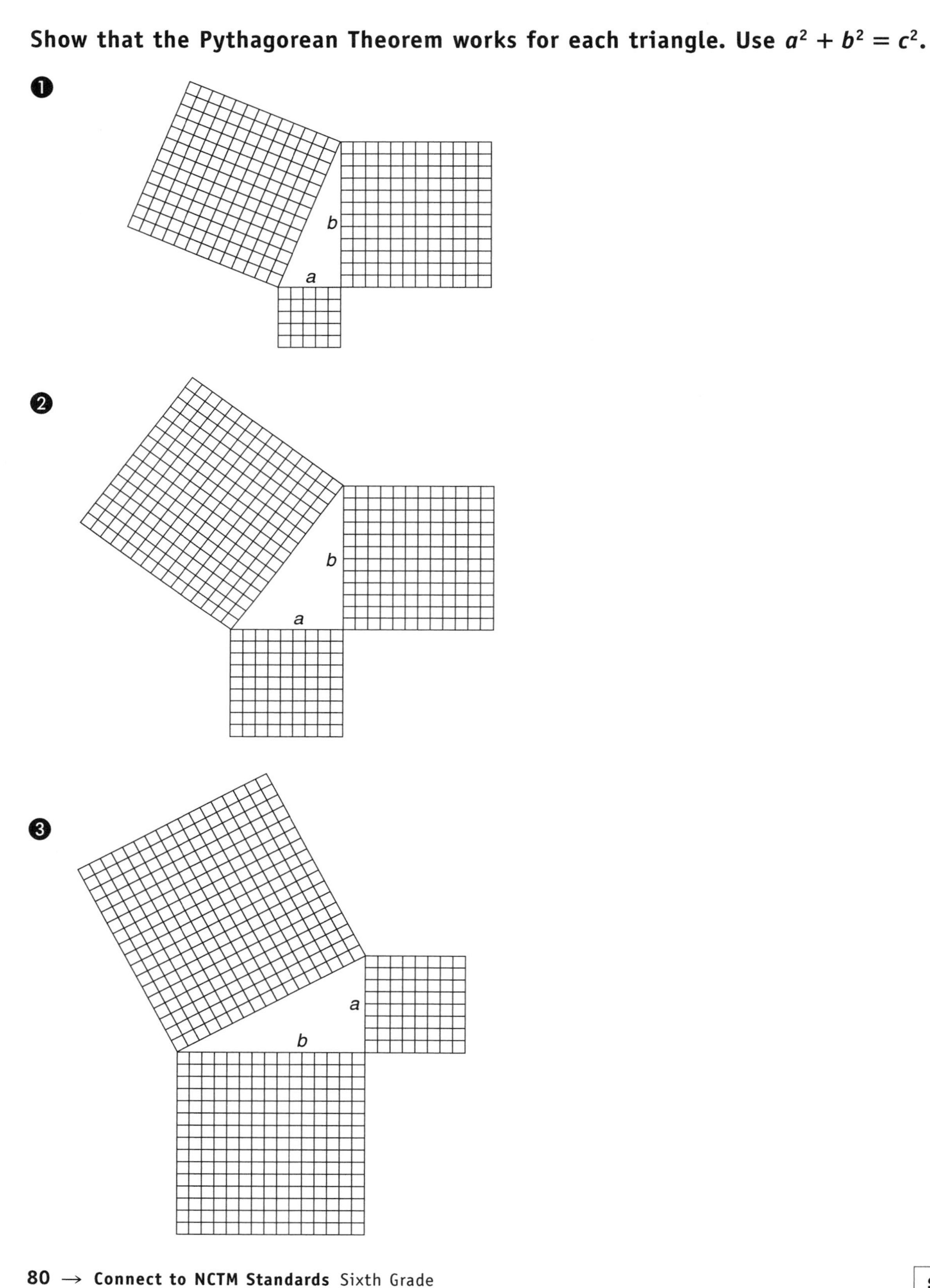

Name ______________________

Demonstrating the Pythagorean Theorem

Label the shorter leg of each right triangle *a*, the longer leg *b*, and the hypotenuse *c*.

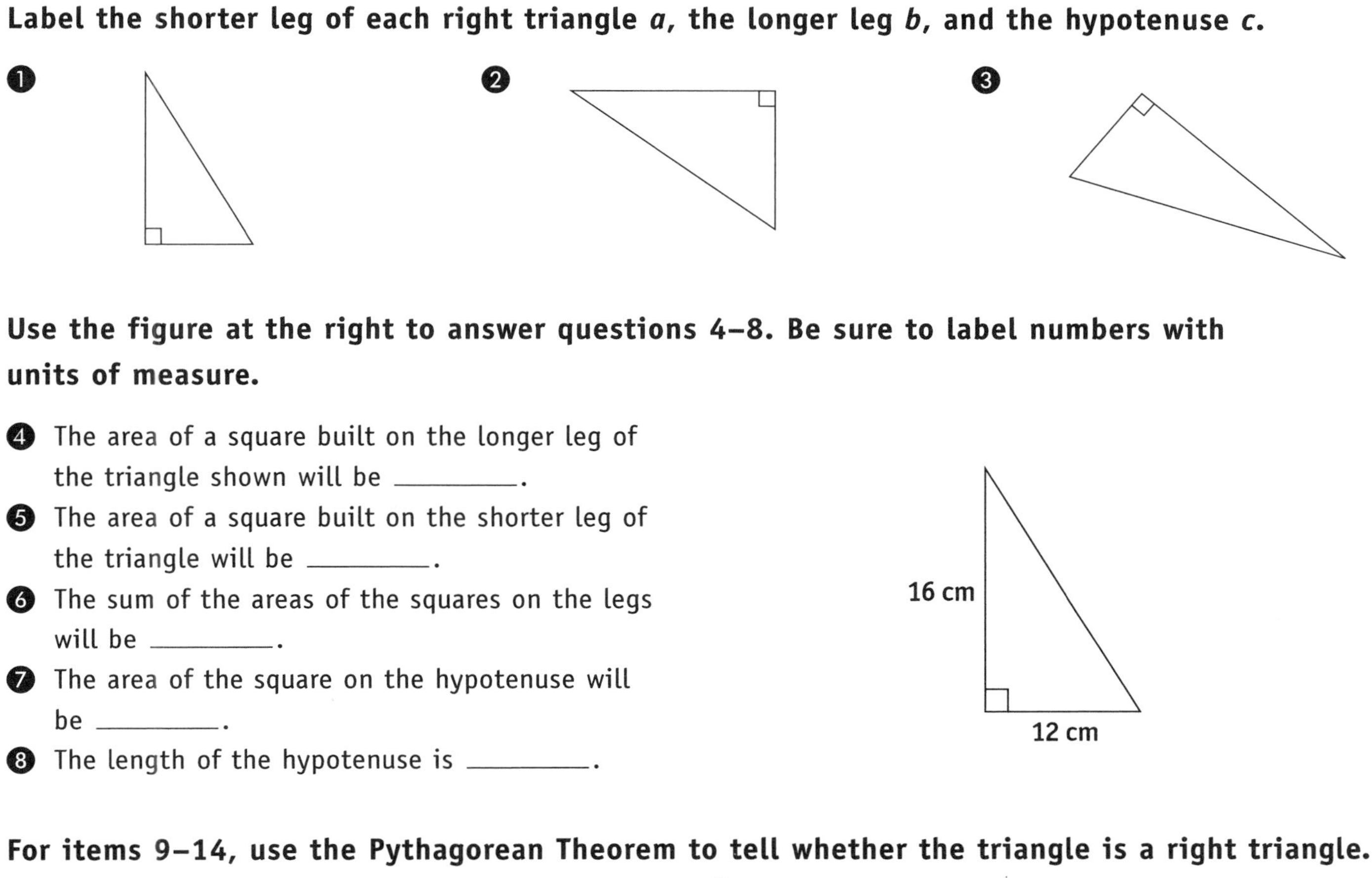

Use the figure at the right to answer questions 4–8. Be sure to label numbers with units of measure.

4. The area of a square built on the longer leg of the triangle shown will be ________.
5. The area of a square built on the shorter leg of the triangle will be ________.
6. The sum of the areas of the squares on the legs will be ________.
7. The area of the square on the hypotenuse will be ________.
8. The length of the hypotenuse is ________.

For items 9–14, use the Pythagorean Theorem to tell whether the triangle is a right triangle.

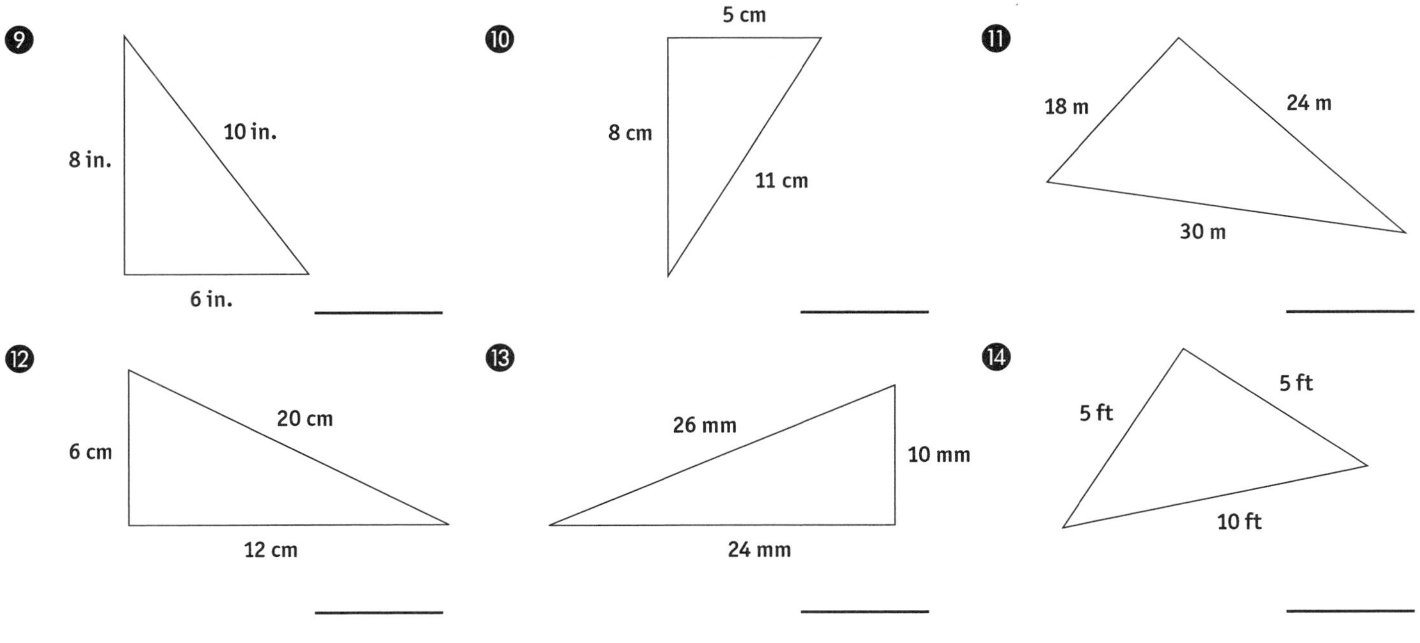

Exploring Possible and Impossible Figures

Introduction

Objective → Students will determine if at least one figure can be drawn to meet a given set of specifications.

Context → Prior to this lesson, students have learned about properties of triangles, quadrilaterals, and other plane figures. They are familiar with the concepts of congruence and similarity and have experience with drawing and measuring angles. Students will go on to investigate properties of solid figures.

NCTM Standards Focus

This lesson provides opportunities for students to apply reasoning and their understanding of plane figures to determine whether specific figures can be created based on features described. By making drawings to test and confirm their thinking, and comparing their visual representations, students gain insight into specific attributes that determine figures and reinforce their understanding of congruence and similarity. Throughout the lesson, students are encouraged to communicate their ideas and apply critical thinking skills as they evaluate the thinking of others.

Representation Students make drawings to fit specifications and analyze the figures represented. Representation supports students' arguments about which figures are possible and which are not.

Reasoning and Proof Students identify whether figures can be drawn as described and if they cannot be drawn, explain why. Students compare and contrast figures resulting from descriptions in which more than one figure can be drawn to specifications. This will help them develop an understanding about what types of specifications completely determine a figure and what types allow flexibility.

Communication As students make conjectures and discuss why certain figures are possible or impossible, they reinforce their understanding of important properties of plane figures. Describing their experiences in trying to draw different figures provides opportunities for them to translate ideas into clear mathematical expression.

Teaching Plan

Materials → Student pages 86–87; centimeter rulers; protractors; straws; pipe cleaners

INTRODUCE THE LESSON by telling students that they will work in pairs. Explain that with their partners, they will explore whether it is possible to draw exactly one figure, more than one figure, or whether a figure cannot be drawn based on information you will provide.

Do you think it is possible to draw a triangle having one side 3 centimeters long, one side 5 centimeters long, and one side 6 centimeters long? Why or why not? Allow for discussion, accepting students' responses without indicating whether they are correct or not. Then, have pairs work together to try to draw the triangle. Students should be successful in producing the figure described since a triangle can be drawn if no side is longer than the sum of the other two sides.

> **What Might Happen . . . What to Do**
>
> **If they cannot create the figure on the first try, some students may think it is not possible. Encourage them to continue their exploration, to draw the lines lightly so they can be erased if need be, and to think about their results and make adjustments accordingly.**

When students are finished, have them compare their work. *Did any students find that they could not draw the triangle? Do all the triangles look the same?* Since the measures of three sides completely determine a triangle, students' drawings should look the same. *Are the triangles you drew congruent?* (Yes.) *How do you know?* (*SSS*) Students can verify that the angles in each of their triangles have approximately the same measures by using a protractor.

NEXT HAVE STUDENTS CONSIDER the possibility of drawing another triangle. *Is it possible to draw a triangle with two angles that measure 40° and one angle that measures 100°? How do you know?* Students should be able to determine that it is possible to draw the figure described since the sum of the measures of the angles equals 180°. Have students draw the triangle using rulers and protractors.

> **What Might Happen . . . What to Do**
>
> **Students may have difficulty knowing how to begin drawing a triangle with specific angle measures. Suggest they draw a straight line and use their protractors to create an angle of required measure from each end of their line. The lines of the angles they make will intersect to create the third angle.**

Have students compare their drawings, which most likely will vary in size from one pair to another. *Do your triangles all look alike? How are they the same? How are they different?* (Triangles have the same shape but different sizes; the measures of the corresponding angles are equal but the lengths of the sides are not.) *Are the triangles you drew congruent?* (No.) *Are they similar?* (Yes.)

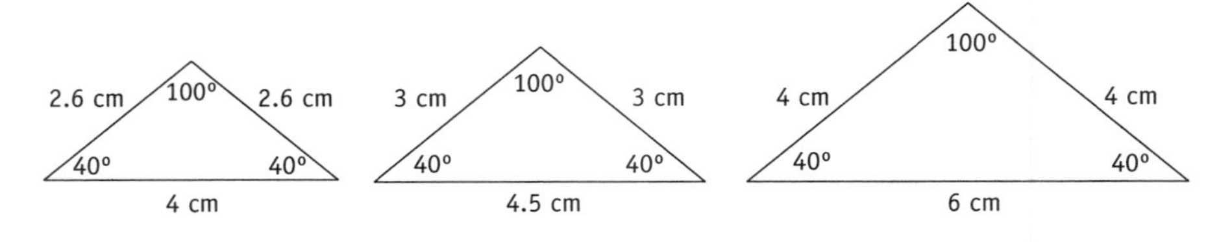

DESCRIBE A THIRD FIGURE for students to consider. *Is it possible to draw a quadrilateral with four angles that each measure 100°? Why or why not?* (No. The sum of the measures of the angles of a quadrilateral must equal 360°.) *What do you think would happen if you tried to draw such a figure?* (The figure would require more than four sides to "close up".) You may wish to give students a few minutes to try to draw the figure and verify that their thinking was correct.

Provide one more exercise. *Is it possible to draw a figure with two sides that measure 3 centimeters and two sides that measure 6 centimeters so that the congruent sides are not parallel? Try it.* Have students compare figures. *What does your figure look like? What is the name given to this figure?* (Student drawings should show a kite.) If any students draw a figure that is not a kite, have the class examine the figure to determine if, in fact, it meets all the stated specifications. This part of the activity provides an excellent opportunity for students to use critical thinking and visual analysis.

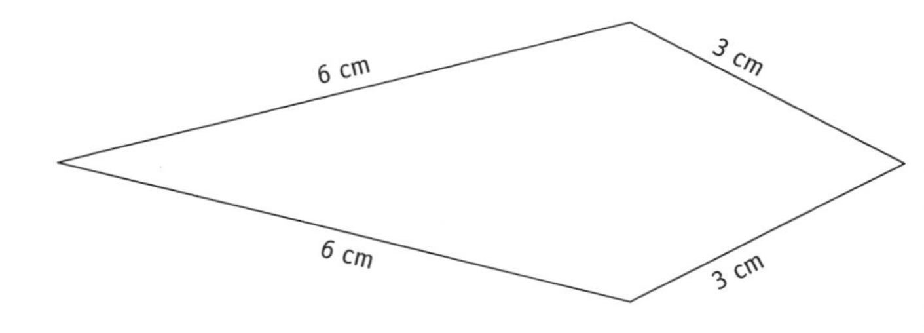

Finally, ask students what they would draw if they were asked to create a simple closed curve with no straight sides. (A freeform, oblong, or circle.)

CONCLUDE THE LESSON by giving students an opportunity to create some of their own sets of specifications for figures. Advise them to be careful to state the conditions clearly. Instruct them to determine whether or not

Answers

Page 86

1–2. Possible solutions—length of third side can vary, and that changes the measure of the other two angles.

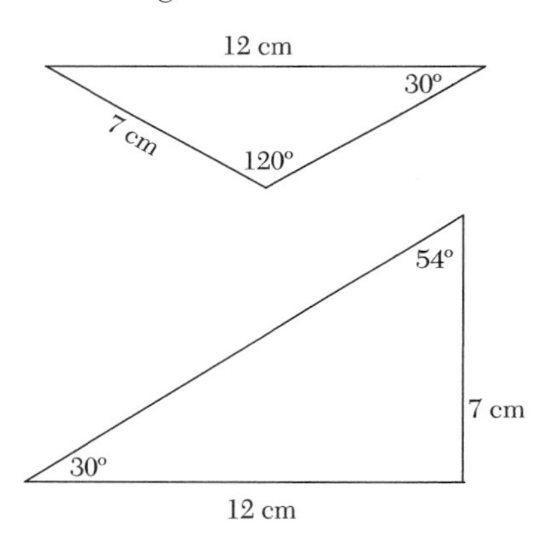

3. Not possible. The 4-cm side cannot reach the third side that comes off of the 30° angle.

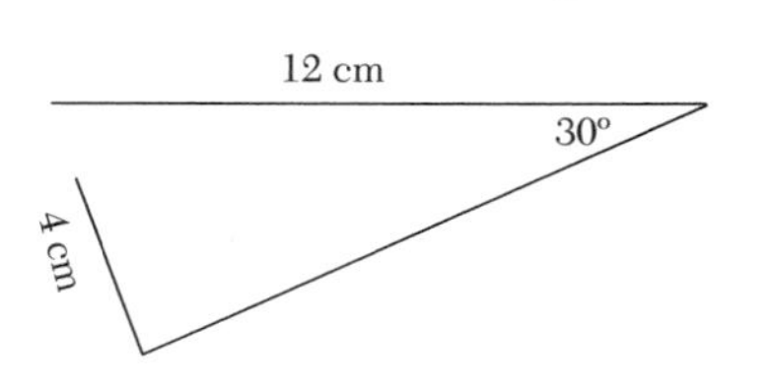

their figures are possible and if more than one drawing may be acceptable. Students can trade papers and solve each other's problems. If time allows, have students share their work in a class discussion.

Student Pages

Student page 86 presents three explorations that are more difficult than the introductory lesson activity. You may wish to allot class time for students to carry out the explorations and discuss their results. If the activities are assigned as homework, allow time for follow-up during a subsequent class. Student page 87 provides additional practice exercises and real-world situations to be analyzed.

Assessment

As students made their drawings and responded to questions about specifications, it was possible to assess their knowledge of key properties of plane figures as well as their proficiency in translating verbal descriptions into visual representations. The explorations and exercises on the student pages provided additional opportunities to evaluate students' abilities to think analytically and apply geometric concepts.

NCTM Standards Summary

The activities in this lesson provided opportunities for students to judge whether or not they could create a specific result from a given list of requirements, a skill that is often needed in the real world. Students supported their answers concerning possible and impossible figures by reasoning and applying their understanding of properties of plane figures. They made drawings to test their thinking and confirm if figures were possible. By comparing visual representations, students gained insight into specific attributes that determine figures and reinforced their understanding of congruence and similarity. In activities with partners as well as in class discussion, students communicated their ideas and were able to listen critically to explanations formulated by others.

Answers

Page 87

1. Possible; equilateral triangle
2. Not possible; sum $< 360°$
3. Possible
4. Possible
5. Possible
6. Impossible; $11 > 6 + 4$
7. Possible; quadrilateral will be non-convex, or concave
8. Possible; circle, oval, simple closed curve
9. Not possible; fourth angle would be 0; not a quadrilateral
10. Possible; 86°, 86°, 8°
11. 5 miles in a straight line; 1 mile in a triangle
12. No, she cannot create a closed triangular garden with those lengths.

Name ______________________

Exploring Possible and Impossible Figures

Solve the problems.

Work with a partner. Using straws cut to the given lengths, or pipe cleaners, try to create the figure described. If you are able to create the figure, trace or sketch it to show your solution. Some figures are not possible. If you are not able to create the figure, write ***not possible*** and explain why. Use another sheet of paper if necessary.

1. Create a triangle with one side 12 cm, one side 7 cm, and the third side of any length. Make the angle opposite the 7-cm side measure 30°.

2. Create a second triangle that fits the same description given in problem 1, but that looks different. Explain what is different about the two triangles.

3. Create a triangle with one side 12 cm, one side 4 cm, and the third side of any length. Make the angle opposite the 4-cm side measure 30°.

Name

Exploring Possible and Impossible Figures

Try to draw each of the figures described. If you think it is not possible to draw the figure described, write *not possible* and give reasons why.

1. A triangle with three angles that each measure 60° and with all its sides the same length.

2. A quadrilateral with angles that measure 70°, 80°, 90°, and 100°.

3. A quadrilateral with sides that measure 4, 8, 9, and 15 centimeters.

4. A triangle with angles that measure 20°, 70°, and 90°.

5. A triangle with sides that measure 5, 12, and 13 centimeters.

6. A triangle with sides that measure 4, 6, and 11 centimeters.

7. A quadrilateral with sides that measure 3, 4, 5, and 15 centimeters.

8. A closed shape with no angles.

9. A quadrilateral with three angles each measuring 120°.

10. A triangle with two angles measuring more than 85°.

11. Paul lives 2 miles from Rita, and Rita lives 3 miles from the shopping mall.
    a) What is the farthest distance that Paul could live from the mall? Explain.
    b) What is the shortest distance that Paul could live from the mall? Explain.

12. Sharon has some boards that measure 3, 4, and 8 feet. Without cutting any of the boards, can Sharon wall off an area in her yard to use as an herb garden? Explain.

Classifying Triangles

Introduction

Objective → Students will classify triangles in terms of sides or angles and find missing angle measures in triangles.

Context → This lesson appears early in a geometry unit. Students are familiar with congruence. They have identified types of angles and will move on to study plane figures, lines, rays, segments, and congruent figures.

Classifying Triangles

Learn

Graphic artists use geometric figures in their work. This design is made with three triangles. The sum of the measurements of a triangle equal 180°.

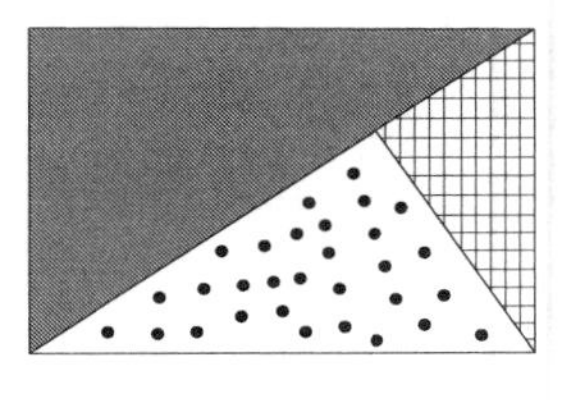

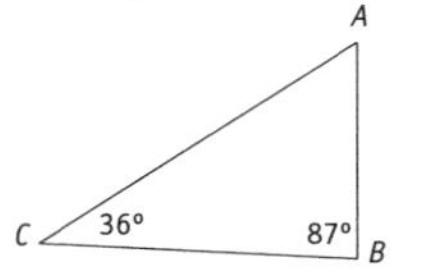

Find the measure of ∠A or ∠BAC.
87° + 36° = 123°
180° − 123° = 57°; *m* ∠*C* = 57°

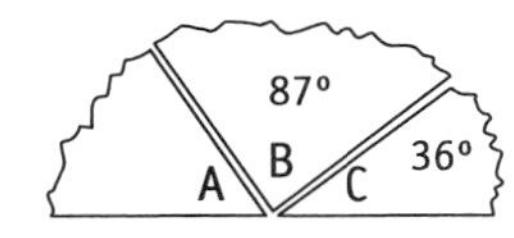

If you tear off the angles of a triangle and put them next to to each other, they form a straight line and measure 180°.

Classifying Triangles

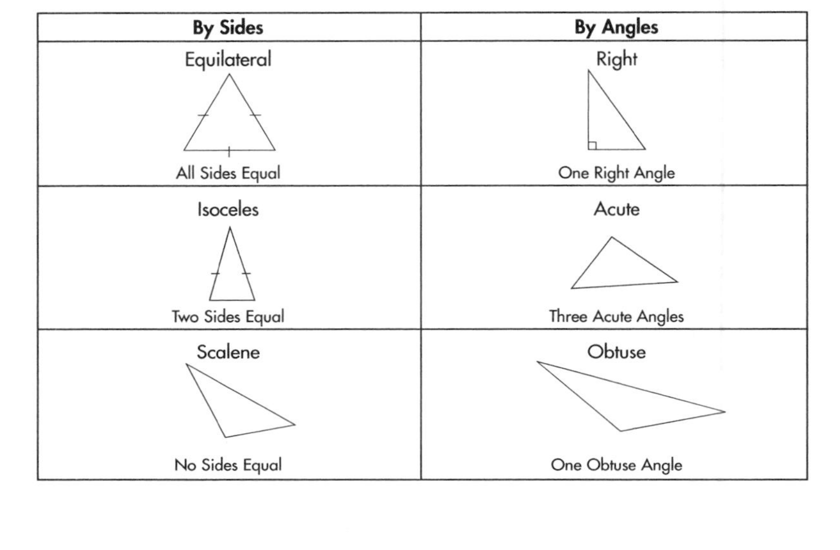

By Sides	By Angles
Equilateral All Sides Equal	Right One Right Angle
Isoceles Two Sides Equal	Acute Three Acute Angles
Scalene No Sides Equal	Obtuse One Obtuse Angle

NCTM Process Standards Analysis and Focus

The standards analysis examines how the process standards have been incorporated into the above lesson. By increasing the focus on three of the process standards, a more effective and meaningful lesson can be presented. The suggestions offered can help you to think about how this might be accomplished.

Reasoning and Proof The lesson includes some good questions that require students to apply their understanding of definitions to find lengths and angle measures. More questions of this type are needed.

Suggestion → **Focus students' thinking on the attributes that characterize each type of triangle. Analyzing features and relationships will help students generalize the characteristics that are**

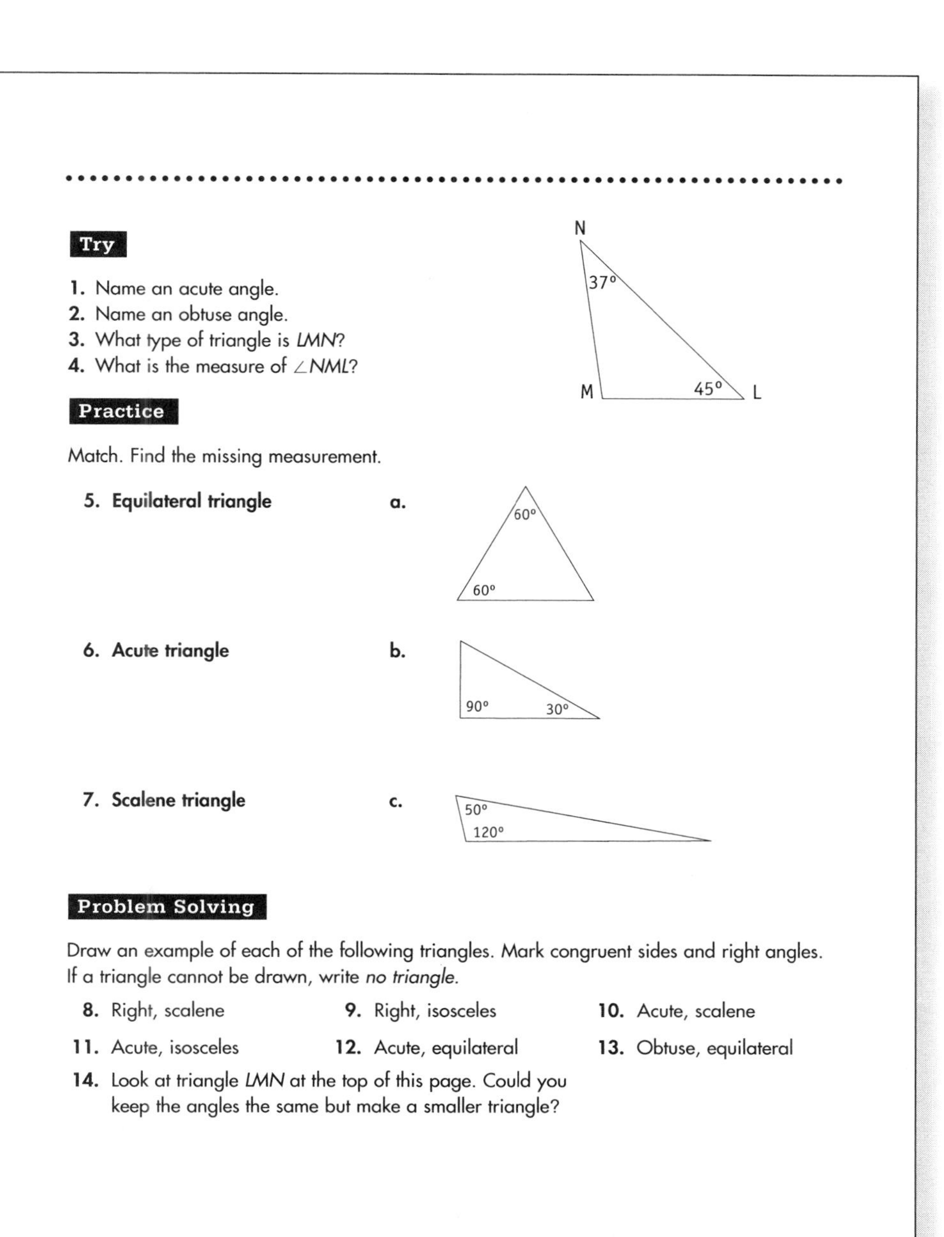

Try

1. Name an acute angle.
2. Name an obtuse angle.
3. What type of triangle is *LMN*?
4. What is the measure of $\angle NML$?

Practice

Match. Find the missing measurement.

5. **Equilateral triangle** a.
6. **Acute triangle** b.
7. **Scalene triangle** c.

Problem Solving

Draw an example of each of the following triangles. Mark congruent sides and right angles. If a triangle cannot be drawn, write *no triangle.*

8. Right, scalene
9. Right, isosceles
10. Acute, scalene
11. Acute, isosceles
12. Acute, equilateral
13. Obtuse, equilateral
14. Look at triangle *LMN* at the top of this page. Could you keep the angles the same but make a smaller triangle?

used to classify triangles. Synthesizing information will enhance geometric reasoning and help students develop definitions that make sense to them.

Connections The lesson refers to the use of triangles in graphic arts and structural design.

Suggestion **→ Assist students in connecting their knowledge about angles to types of triangles. This will help them discern attributes of triangles as they reason through developing their own definitions.**

Communication A good question is posed at the end of the lesson, but the entire concept development proceeds without opportunities for students to discuss and contribute ideas.

Suggestion **→ Provide opportunities for discussion to help students differentiate relevant attributes (such as side and angle measures) from irrelevant attributes (such as overall size and orientation). Creating definitions in this way will lead to better understanding and retention of the terms and attributes associated with each type of triangle.**

Problem Solving Questions labeled as problem solving are, in fact, reasoning and proof.

Representation The lesson presents geometric drawings and asks students to identify missing measurements. Students are also asked to represent different types of triangles with their own drawings.

The teaching plan that follows shows how the suggestions for increasing the focus on the process standards can be implemented.

Revised Teaching Plan

BEGIN THE LESSON with a brief discussion of how objects can be classified by common attributes or properties. For example, a collection of books could be sorted according to topic, author, color of cover, weight, price, and so on. Point out that some classifications are more useful than others.

Inform students that there are two ways triangles are classified: one way is by their angles, and the other is by the lengths of their sides. Explain that these classifications help us study and communicate general information about triangles. Then write the six types of triangles on the board, putting them into two groups. Encourage students to use prior geometric knowledge. *Which of these names do you think describe the triangles by their angles? Explain.*

CONDUCT A BRIEF REVIEW of acute, obtuse, and right angles. Then help students connect the different angles to triangle classification. Begin by exploring the relationships that exist between right angles and right triangles. *What kind of angle(s) do you think a right triangle would have?* (A right angle) *What does a right triangle look like?* Invite students to draw right triangles on the board, and ask the class to verify that each drawing is a right triangle. Ask if any student can draw a right triangle that looks different from those on the board. Seeing different representations will help students realize that right triangles do not all have to look the same.

CONTINUE POSING QUESTIONS. *Can a right triangle have two right angles? How can you be sure? Can a triangle with a right angle also have an obtuse angle?* (No.) *Explain.* (At least four sides would be required to close a figure having two right angles or a right angle and an obtuse angle.) Encourage students to prove their conclusions by using logic or drawings. Through this type of reasoning and discussion, students will improve their understanding of the relationships among the angles in each type of triangle and extend their geometric intuition.

What Might Happen . . . What to Do

Students often have difficulty identifying a right triangle if the right angle is not at the base. Point out that turning a square does not change its "squareness." Similarly, position or orientation does not matter for a right triangle. Show students a right triangle with the right angle at the vertex opposite the base, and ask how they might determine if the triangle is a right triangle. Students may suggest that they can change the orientation or tell visually. Explain that the convention is to use a little "square" to identify the right angle. Without this indication, the right angle could only be verified by measuring it.

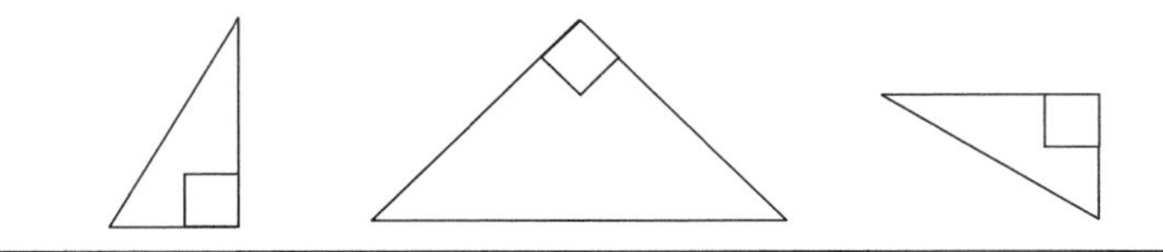

HAVE STUDENTS DRAW a right triangle. *What statement can be made about the size of the other two angles?* It should be obvious that each of the other angles is less than 90°, that is, acute. Ask students to draw different right triangles, ranging from one that has two equal sides that meet at the right angle to one that has one very long side and one short side, and to observe the other two angles. They should notice that as one angle increases in size, the other decreases, but that the larger angle can never reach 90°. Explain that the sum of the measures of the three angles is always 180°. A nice way to demonstrate this fact would be to show students how to mark the angles of triangles, cut the angles off, and place the vertices together to see that they form a straight angle, which, by definition, is 180°. You might consider distributing several triangles of different sizes and shapes to groups of students and asking them to verify this fact.

Ask questions that have students apply this information. *If a right triangle has one angle measuring 90°, what must be true about the other two angles? Explain.* (180° − 90° = 90°; the two angles total 90°.) *If one angle of a right triangle measures 30°, what is the measure of the third angle? How do you know?* (60°; 90° + 30° = 120°; subtract 120° from the total 180° to get the third angle measure.)

SHIFT STUDENTS' FOCUS to obtuse triangles. *How do you recognize an obtuse triangle?* (It has an obtuse angle.) *Could a triangle have more than one obtuse angle?* (No.) *How can you prove this?* Students should be able to explain that the sum of three angles in a triangle is exactly 180° and two obtuse angles together are already more than 180°. *What statement could be made about the other two angles in an obtuse triangle?* (Both must be acute.) *Explain.* (Their sum must be less than 90°, and so each of the other angles must be acute.)

Next, prompt students to think about acute triangles. Ask students how they think an acute triangle might be identified. *Could an acute triangle have a right angle? Why or why not? What about an obtuse angle?* Students should be able to articulate that if a triangle had a right angle, it would be a right triangle, and if it had an obtuse angle, it would be an obtuse triangle. Consequently, acute triangles have three acute angles. This discussion will help students remember the attributes of each type of triangle.

Summarize classifying triangles by angles by having students define each type of triangle. Write the definitions on the board, and have students copy them into their notebooks.

f.y.i.

The term *equilateral* comes from two Latin words: *aequi*, meaning "equal," and *latus*, meaning "side."

MOVE ON TO A DISCUSSION about triangles classified by their sides. Help students connect the word *equilateral* with a figure having sides of equal length. Then define the other terms, *isosceles* and *scalene*, for the class. Emphasize that to classify triangles by sides, it is necessary to examine the relationships among all three sides. Have students copy definitions into their notebooks as above.

WRAP UP THE LESSON by displaying six to nine triangles, making sure to represent each type. Ask students first to identify each triangle according to the length of its sides. Then ask them to identify each according to its angles. Record the information next to each triangle. Pose questions about possible side and angle combinations, and ask students to justify their responses. Doing this will help students understand that triangles can belong to more than one general class. *Can a triangle be both acute and isosceles?* (Yes.) *Right and scalene*? (Yes.) *Equilateral and obtuse*? (No.) *Isosceles and equilateral*? (Yes.) This last question will help students make the logical distinction that equilateral triangles must have three equal sides and in order to have three equal sides, they must have two equal sides. Therefore, all equilateral triangles must be isosceles. However, not all isosceles triangles need to be equilateral.

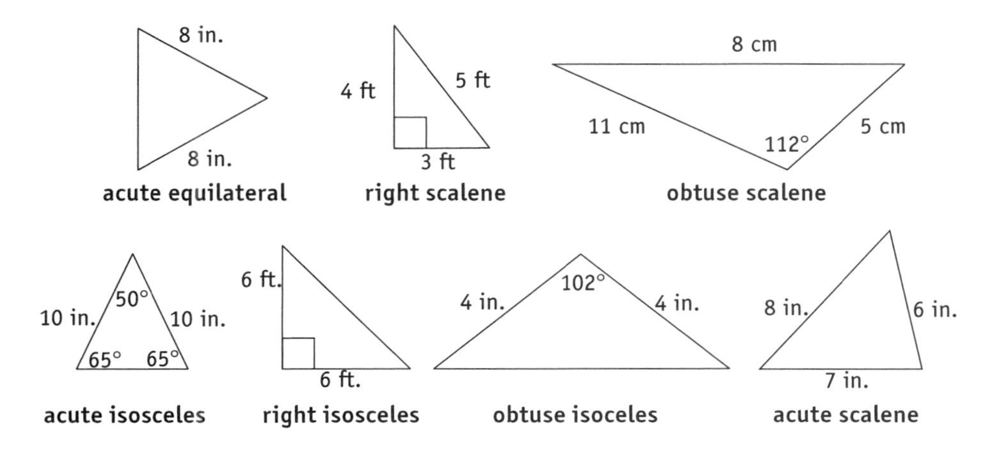

Student Pages

Students are now ready to complete exercises similar to those on the reduced student pages. Point out that students should base their work on the measures given, not the visual appearance of triangles.

Assessment

There were opportunities to assess students' understanding of triangle classification as they responded to questions and made drawings. By noting their reasoning processes during oral exercises, you could evaluate students' ability to apply the result about the sum of the measures of the angles of a triangle.

NCTM Standards Summary

Discussing the different types of angles helped students connect their knowledge to the names used to classify triangles by angle measures. In this way, the names became more meaningful for students and more likely to be remembered. Through their own reasoning about the attributes of different types of triangles, students were able to extend their knowledge about triangle relationships and formulate their own definitions. Asking students to explain their thinking as they found missing angle measurements reinforced the connection to the total degrees in the angles of a triangle. Opportunities for thinking about and discussing possible combined classifications enabled students to recognize that figures can belong to more than one general class and to make important logical distinctions.

Standard 4 **Measurement**

AT THE SIXTH GRADE LEVEL, measurement includes work with angles, scale drawings, circles, and customary and metric units. Our lessons are derived from these important topics, and include a lesson on recognizing angles, a lesson on creating a scale drawing, a lesson that explores using circles, and a lesson on converting metric measures to other metric units.

Three lessons model how the process standards can be used to teach content. A fourth lesson is a hypothetical textbook lesson that we have revised to be more standards based. These four lessons do not represent the entire curriculum, but rather provide glimpses of how, with a more concentrated effort to incorporate the process standards, better mathematics teaching and learning can be achieved.

In one lesson we have chosen, students measure angles and classify them by their measure. Students represent angles using manipulatives, by making drawings, and by recognizing them in their environment. Through opportunities for communication, students reinforce their fluency with the vocabulary for classifying angles. Students use reasoning and proof to answer questions about the relationships between the types of angles.

Another lesson we have chosen has students creating a detailed scale drawing. Using the process standards of problem solving, representation, and communication, students determine an appropriate scale for their model, and develop a method for placing objects accurately on their drawing. Students reinforce their skills by interpreting each other's drawings.

A third lesson that we have chosen is one in which students solve problems that involve using circles. Using the process standards of problem solving, reasoning and proof, and communication, students work to improve their problem-solving skills.

The hypothetical textbook lesson we have chosen to revise is one that explores converting metric measures to other metric units. Through better incorporation of the process standards of connections, representation, and communication, students learn all, rather than some, of the metric prefixes from milli- to kilo-, and how they relate in a place value chart. Increased discussion about the relationships helps students avoid some of the common misconceptions that can develop. Some history of the metric system is presented to provide added interest.

Standard 4 Lessons

Recognizing Angles

Making a Scale Drawing

Using Circles

Converting Among Metric Units

Recognizing Angles

Introduction

Objective → Students will measure angles and classify them according to their measure.

Context → Students know the geometric definition of angle as two rays with a common endpoint. After learning how to measure and classify angles, they will go on to use protractors and compasses to measure, copy, and bisect angles. They will also use angle relationships and learn about parallel lines.

NCTM Standards Focus

In this activity-based lesson, students will develop spatial sense about the size of different angles. They will extend their understanding to measuring angles in degrees and classifying them using precise mathematical terms. As students become more proficient at analyzing angles abstractly, they will also create their own references for estimating angle measures.

Representation Students make drawings of angles and use manipulatives to represent angles. They also identify angles represented in real-world contexts.

Reasoning and Proof Students use reasoning to apply the system of informal angle classification without measuring. They recognize that the categories are mutually exclusive, and they use this concept to justify their responses to questions.

Communication Students organize their mathematical thinking about angles and develop the vocabulary necessary to communicate their thoughts to others, both informally and through precise mathematical terms. As students discuss real-world representations of angles, they reinforce their understanding of angle concepts.

Teaching Plan

Materials → Student pages 100–101; two paper plates (one white, one colored) for each student; scissors; protractors

BEGIN THE LESSON BY INTRODUCING informal definitions of angles that give students a basis of comparison.

- A right angle is a corner, like the angle formed by two walls.
- A straight angle is a line, like the base of one wall.
- An acute angle is smaller than a right angle.
- An obtuse angle is larger than a right angle but smaller than a straight angle.

Distribute paper plates and scissors to students and have them make "angle makers." Demonstrate how to carefully cut a straight line from the edge of each plate to the center. Show how to insert the white plate into the colored plate, laying the two flat. Explain that by rotating the plates, students can use their angle maker to represent angles of different sizes.

Allow students to experiment with their angle makers, then ask them to use their angle makers to model each type of angle. Have students compare their representations after modeling each type of angle. *Are all right angles the same size?* (Yes.) *What other type of angle is always the same size?* (Straight angles) *Are all acute angles the same size?* (No.) *What other type of angle can have different sizes?* (Obtuse angles can vary in size.) Have students select angles in the room; identify the angles they name as greater than, equal to, or smaller than a right angle; and approximate the angles on their angle makers. Modeling the angles will affirm students' sense of the sizes of acute, right, and obtuse angles.

Reinforce the idea of classifying angles with a discussion of clock angles. Point out that as the clock hands move, the angle formed by the hour hand and the minute hand is constantly changing. Use an actual clock face or draw pictures on the board to represent different times. *What kind of angle do the hands of the clock form at 1:00 p.m.?* (Acute) *3:00 p.m.?* (Right) *6:00 a.m.?* (Straight) *8:00 a.m.?* (Obtuse) Describe the change in the angle formed by the clock hands as the time goes from 11:00 a.m. to 11:20 a.m. Make a sketch. (The angle formed by the hands changes from an acute angle to an obtuse angle.) *What about between 9:00 p.m. and 9:40 p.m.?* (The angle changes from a right angle to an acute angle.)

Distribute student page 100. Direct students to Part A and direct them to use their informal understanding to classify each angle pictured as acute, right, obtuse, or straight. When students have finished the identification, briefly go over the classifications and answer any questions.

Introduce the idea of actual angle measure. Explain that angles are measured in degrees (°) and that the measurement tool for angles is a protractor. Provide students with protractors and model how they are used.

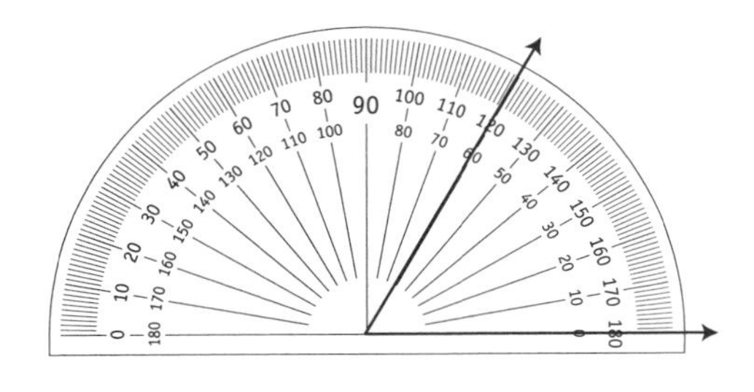

Step 1 Place the center arrow of the protractor on the point where the two rays meet.

f.y.i.

Help students remember the different types of angles by telling them that they always carry with them a "handy" protractor. Have students spread their fingers as wide as possible. *What type of angle do your thumb and forefinger form?* (Right angle) *What type of angle is formed between any other two fingers?* (Acute angle) *What type of angle is formed between the thumb and any other finger except the forefinger?* (Obtuse angle)

Step 2 Place the zero edge of the protractor on one side of the angle.

Step 3 Read the scale on the protractor.

NOW HAVE STUDENTS use their protractors to find the actual measure of the angles in Part A on the student page. When they have completed the measuring, engage them in a discussion that will help students connect the classification of angles with their measures. *What measure describes a right angle?* (90°) *What measure describes a straight angle?* (180°) *How would you define an acute angle to express it in terms of degrees?* (An acute angle measures less than 90°.) *How can you define an obtuse angle to express it in terms of degrees? Explain.* (Since an obtuse angle is greater than a right angle but smaller than a straight angle, the measure of an obtuse angle is greater than 90° but less than 180°.) Noting and defining these relationships for themselves will make the results more meaningful to students.

What Might Happen . . . What to Do

Students might be confused by the two sets of numbers on the protractor and may use the wrong set of numbers to identify the measure of a given angle. For example, they may record the measure of a 60° angle as 120°. Remind students that looking at the angle and considering its general classification will help them to decide which band of numbers to use. An acute angle must be less than 90°, and therefore, cannot have a measure of 120°.

Ask students to draw any four angles at random, then classify each angle just by looking at it. Have students trade drawings and actually measure the angles that have been drawn, write the measures, and indicate if they agree or disagree with the classification. This brief activity will improve students' sense of angle size and provide added practice in classifying angles.

CONCLUDE THE LESSON by having students think about the following problem. *After measuring an angle, a student made the following statement: "This angle measures less than an obtuse angle, so it must be an acute angle." Was the student's statement correct? Explain why you agree or disagree.* (The statement was not correct; a right angle measures less than an obtuse angle and a right angle is not an acute angle.)

Extension

Have students use a street map of their city or a city they would like to visit, such as San Francisco or Washington, D.C. Ask them to measure and classify the angles formed by different pairs of intersecting streets. Encourage them to find as many examples as they can of each type of angle. Encourage them to indicate the pair of streets that formed the greatest angle, the smallest angle, the angle closest to 70°, and so on.

Student Pages

Part A of student page 100 includes the angle drawings that students will measure and classify during the lesson and statements for students to complete to summarize definitions. Part B asks students to read the measures of angles superimposed on a protractor and to classify the angles. Student page 101 presents practice exercises involving measuring and classifying angles.

Assessment

As students identified and modeled different angles based on informal definitions, it was possible to gauge their understanding of the terms being used. As the lesson continued, you could note students who were able to classify the angles according to measure and measure angles accurately using protractors. Students' responses to questions during discussion served as indicators of their understanding of the formal definitions.

NCTM Standards Summary

Representing angles both with manipulatives and drawings helped students to differentiate between angles of different sizes and give meaning to angle classification. Students used reasoning to restate their informal understandings about angle types as precise mathematical definitions in terms of measures. They applied the classification system and thought critically about statements involving angles. Through discussion, students communicated their understandings of the different types of angles and examples of angles represented by real-world objects.

Answers

Page 100

1. Right; 90°
2. Straight; 180°
3. Acute; 35°
4. Obtuse; 125°
5. 90°
6. 180°
7. 90°
8. 90°; 180°
9. 25°; acute
10. 50°; acute
11. 65°; acute
12. 90°; right
13. 115°; obtuse
14. 140°; obtuse
15. 155°; obtuse
16. 180°; straight

Page 101

1. 45°; acute
2. 90°; right
3. 135°; obtuse
4. 40°; acute
5. 90°; right
6. 50°; acute
7. 120°; obtuse
8. 60°; acute
9. 80°; acute
10. 145°; obtuse
11. 90°; right
12. 125°; obtuse
13. Both angles must be acute; any other combination would produce a sum greater than 90°.
14. No; The sum of two angles less than 90° must be less than 180°. The angles can both be right or one can be acute and the other obtuse.

Name ______________________

Recognizing Angles

Part A: Classify each angle as acute, right, obtuse, or straight. Then measure each angle.

❶ ______________ ______________

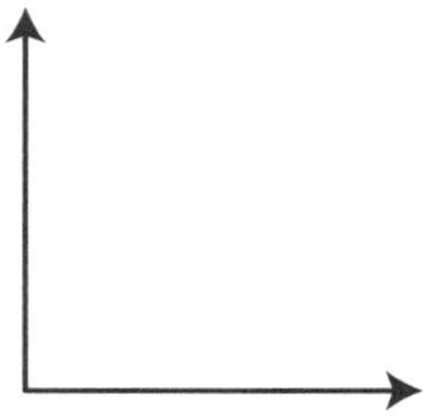

❷ ______________ ______________

❸ ______________ ______________

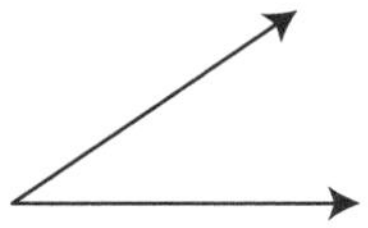

❹ ______________ ______________

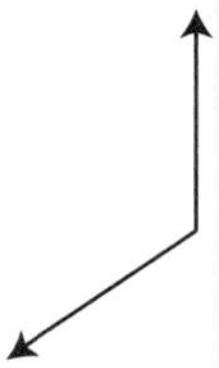

Write the number of degrees to complete each definition.

❺ A right angle measures _____.

❻ A straight angle measures _____.

❼ The measure of an acute angle is less than _____.

❽ The measure of an obtuse angle is greater than _____ but less than _____.

Part B: Use the drawing of a protractor to find the measure of each angle. Then classify each angle as acute, right, obtuse, or straight.

❾ $m\angle AOB$ __________

❿ $m\angle AOC$ __________

⓫ $m\angle AOD$ __________

⓬ $m\angle AOE$ __________

⓭ $m\angle AOF$ __________

⓮ $m\angle AOG$ __________

⓯ $m\angle AOH$ __________

⓰ $m\angle AOJ$ __________

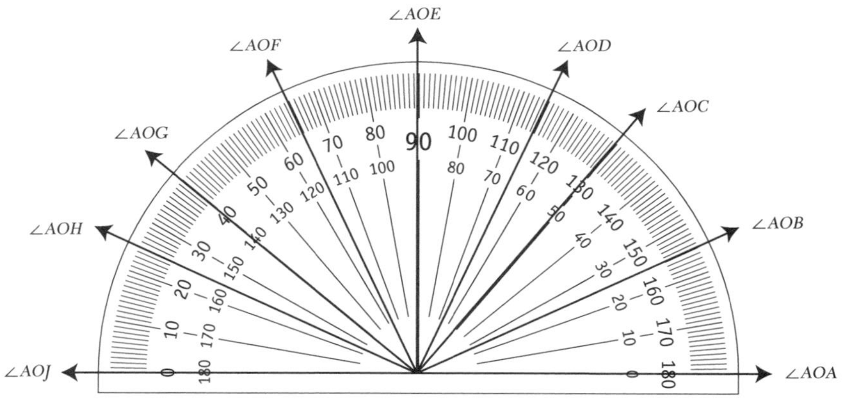

∠AOE

∠AOF ∠AOD

∠AOG ∠AOC

∠AOH ∠AOB

∠AOJ ∠AOA

Name ___________________________

Recognizing Angles

Use the drawings below. Write acute, right, obtuse, or straight to identify each angle. Then use a protractor and find the actual measure of each angle.

❶

❷

❸

Measure each angle in the figure below. Classify each angle as acute, right, obtuse, or straight.

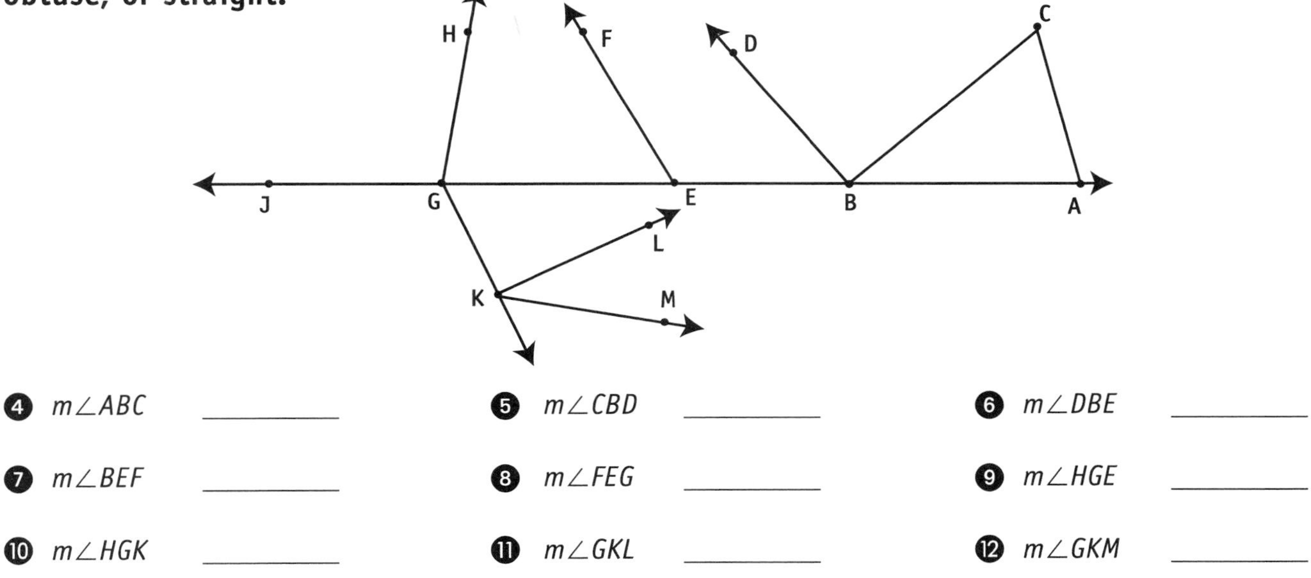

❹ $m\angle ABC$ __________ ❺ $m\angle CBD$ __________ ❻ $m\angle DBE$ __________

❼ $m\angle BEF$ __________ ❽ $m\angle FEG$ __________ ❾ $m\angle HGE$ __________

❿ $m\angle HGK$ __________ ⓫ $m\angle GKL$ __________ ⓬ $m\angle GKM$ __________

⓭ If the sum of two angles is 90°, what type of angle must each be? Explain.

⓮ If the sum of two angles is 180°, can both angles be acute? Explain.

Making a Scale Drawing

Introduction

Objective → Students will create a detailed scale drawing.

Context → Students have used tools to measure length, solve proportions, and interpret scale drawings. They will continue to use ratio and proportion in the study of similar figures, percent, and probability.

NCTM Standards Focus

In this lesson, students will solve problems that involve creating a detailed scale drawing. They will consider how to choose an appropriate scale and will develop a method for positioning objects accurately in their drawings. Students will employ measurement skills and proportion as they gather and convert information to a visual representation that is useful to others.

Problem Solving Students will identify and solve practical problems as they work to make a scale drawing. They will explore positioning items in drawings by solving a simple problem involving a drawing of their desktop. Then they will extend their method to more complex situations.

Representation Students will represent information about the real world visually through a scale drawing. They will convert three-dimensional objects into two-dimensional representations and will reinforce their skills by interpreting each other's drawings.

Communication Students will work cooperatively to complete the different tasks involved in making their drawing. They will share their ideas on finding position and discuss ways in which scale drawings are used to communicate information.

Teaching Plan

Materials → Student pages 106–107; rulers; grid paper (optional)

BEGIN THE LESSON with a brief discussion about scale drawings and how they are used.

- *What is a scale drawing?* (A drawing in which all the dimensions are reduced or enlarged proportionally.)
- *What are some common examples of scale drawings?* (Maps; blueprints; building or room plans; directions for assembling models clothing patterns; etc.)
- *What does the scale of the drawing represent?* (The ratio between any actual length and the corresponding length in the drawing)
- *If you know the scale of a drawing, how can you find an actual length from the length in the drawing, or an unknown length for a drawing from an actual length?* (Write and solve a proportion using the scale as one ratio.)

Present a few problems for students to solve to reinforce students' skills in setting up ratios and finding proportions. Discuss each solution and demonstrate the proportion method for solving the problem.

Suppose the scale of a drawing is $\frac{1}{2}$ in. = 4 ft. The length of a wall on the drawing is $1\frac{3}{4}$ in. What is the actual length of the wall?

$\left(\frac{\frac{1}{2}\text{ in.}}{4} = \frac{1\frac{3}{4}\text{ in.}}{n}; \frac{1}{2}n = 1\frac{3}{4} \times 4; n = 14\text{ ft.}\right)$

Suppose the scale of a map is 2 cm = 25 km. The actual distance between two towns is 80 km. What length would represent this distance on the map? Explain your work. $\left(\frac{2\text{ cm}}{25\text{ km}} = \frac{n\text{ cm}}{80\text{ km}}\right)$

Provide additional examples if students require more practice writing and solving the proportions.

Explain that when someone decides to make a scale drawing, they must first solve several problems. Perhaps the most important problem is deciding on the scale that will be used for the drawing. *What factors would you think about to choose a scale for a drawing? Explain.*

What Students Might Say

- The drawing needs to fit on the paper being used.
- The ratio should be easy to work with.
- The ratio should allow reasonably precise lengths to be represented and then determined by people using the drawing.
- The purpose and amount of detail of the drawing may be a factor—a drawing used to illustrate an apartment might not need to be as detailed and precise as a drawing used to construct the apartment.

DISTRIBUTE STUDENT PAGE 106 and have students work in pairs. Ask them to clear a desktop and then place one or two simple objects such as a book, juice container, or a calculator on the desk. Explain that their assignment will be to create a scale drawing of their desktop that will fit in the given space on student page 106. The objects must be drawn to scale and positioned accurately on the drawing. Questions to help students organize their work will be found on the page.

Circulate among the groups as they work on their drawings and help students who are having difficulty with the positioning aspect. You may wish to have students that finish early offer assistance to other pairs.

Engage students in a discussion of their methods and point out similarities in the scales used by different groups.

- *What scale did you use?*
- *Did you try some scales that you decided not to use? Explain.*
- *Explain the method you used to position the objects accurately on your drawing.*

Have students compare classmates' desktops and drawings. Encourage students to describe and/or demonstrate their approaches. If no student mentions it, suggest that to position items, they should first measure the lengths at right angles from edges of the object to edges of the desk and convert the actual lengths to drawing lengths in the scale being used. Next, lightly pencil in guide lines until there are enough reference points to draw the scaled objects correctly positioned. Have the class decide which methods seemed the most efficient and let them practice by using objects on their desks.

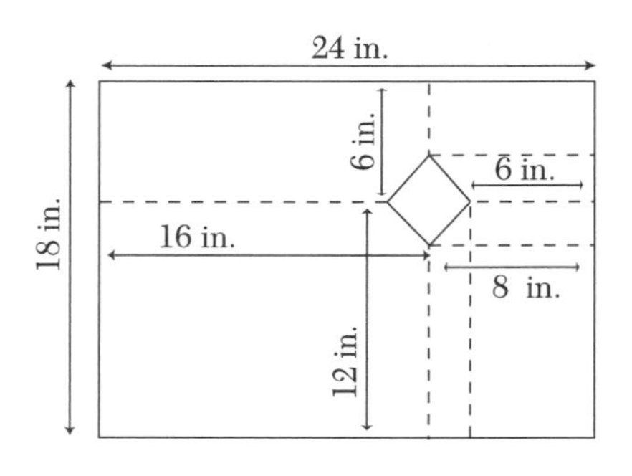

Tell students that having dealt with some of the problems that are involved in making scale drawings for a simple situation, they will go on to deal with a much more challenging problem of creating a scale drawing of the classroom (or another location in the school).

Divide the students into larger groups of four to six and let them spend the remainder of the class time planning the work on this project. They will need to decide on the details they will include in their drawing, the scale they will use, the measurements needed, and the responsibility of each group member. The drawing should be made on a separate sheet of unlined or grid paper; the largest size sheet available should be provided. You may wish to set up a schedule for different groups to take their measurements, and allot class time for completion and discussion of the drawings.

Extension

Encourage students to bring in maps or scale drawings and ask them to write one or two problems based on the materials they are using. Students can trade problems with a classmate to solve.

As an interesting challenge, show students a map of their state from which the scale has been deleted. Supply the actual distances between one or more pairs of major cities. Have students use the information and their own measurements to determine the scale that was used and then compare their results with the actual scale.

Student Pages

Student page 106 provides questions to guide students as they work on the classroom desktop activity, plus space for their scale drawings. Student page 107 presents detailed information about a room and its furnishings. This information provides an opportunity for additional practice with scale computations. Students might then use their scaled dimensions to design the room of their choice.

Assessment

As students reviewed their knowledge of scale drawings, you were able to assess their understanding of the concept and their facility with ratios and proportions. Students' insights into a problem-solving situation could be evaluated as they planned and created their drawings. As they explained their ideas about the class activity and their computational methods, you were able to judge their proficiency in carrying out the measuring, converting, and positioning. When students worked cooperatively on the larger project, you could observe their ability to structure a complex assignment. Their final scale drawing provided an opportunity for overall assessment of their proficiency with this topic.

NCTM Standards Summary

In this activity-based lesson, students identified and solved problems related to making an accurate scale drawing. By first working on a simple problem, students gained experience choosing a scale and developed their own methods for representing objects. In sharing their methods, students communicated useful information to others and affirmed their own understanding of the processes involved. Communication also reinforced understanding of the computational skills involved in creating and interpreting scale drawings.

Answers

Page 106
Answers will vary.

Page 107
Scale dimensions
Living room: 5.5 in. × 3.25 in.
Windows: 0.55 in.
Entry: 1 in.
Sofa: 1.5 in. × 0.5 in.
Easy chairs: 0.6 in. × 0.45 in.
Rocking chair: 0.35 in. × 0.57 in.
Table: 0.7 in. × 0.65 in.
Plant stand: 0.35 in. × 0.3 in.
Entertainment: 0.9 in. × 0.4 in.

Name ________________________________

Making a Scale Drawing

Place 2 or 3 items on your desktop. Answer the questions about your arrangement and then make a scale drawing of your desktop in the space below. Use the back of this page for calculations and notes.

❶ Record the actual length of your desk.

❷ Record the actual width.

❸ Name the object(s) you will you show on your drawing. Give the actual dimensions of each object.

❹ Write the scale you will use for your drawing. Explain how you chose this scale.

❺ Record the length your desk will be in your scale drawing. Show how you found this measurement.

❻ Record the width your desk will be in your scale drawing. Show how you found this measurement.

❼ Explain the method you used to determine the position of the objects in your drawing.

Name ______________________

Making a Scale Drawing

Use the information provided to create a scale drawing.

The Benson's have the following information about their new living room:

- The room is 27.5 feet long and 16.25 feet wide.
- Along the length of the room are two equally spaced windows. Each window is 33 inches wide.
- There is a 5-foot entry space along the side of the room facing the windows.

The Benson's would like to put the following furniture in their room:

- A sofa that is 90 inches long and 30 inches deep
- Two easy chairs that are each 36 inches wide and 27 inches deep
- A rocking chair that is 21 inches wide and 34 inches deep
- A table that is 42 inches long and 39 inches deep
- A plant stand that is 21 inches wide and 18 inches deep
- An entertainment unit that is 54 inches wide and 24 inches deep

Give the scale-drawing measurements of the room and each piece of furniture. Show a possible arrangement of the furniture in your scale drawing.

Scale: 1 inch = 5 feet

living room ______________

windows ______________

entry ______________

sofa ______________

easy chairs ______________

rocking chair ______________

table ______________

plant stand ______________

entertainment unit ______________

Using Circles

Introduction

Objective → Students will solve problems involving circles and suggest related problems to explore.

Context → This lesson comes after students have learned to find perimeter and area for quadrilaterals, triangles, and circles. Students have worked with fractions, ratios, and percents. They will go on to study volume and surface area of solid figures.

NCTM Standards Focus

In this lesson, problems involving circles and other figures require students to make a plan and organize the information needed to solve the problem. Students will discover that solving one problem raises other interesting questions that can lead to different paths of exploration. Students will participate in a problem-solving experience that reflects the true nature of mathematics as they look for patterns in their work and suggest alternative situations.

Problem Solving Students break down a complex problem into smaller parts and decide how to work with each part. They consider alternate strategies and evaluate the effectiveness of each. As students focus on the meaning of their solution, they recognize other related problems.

Reasoning and Proof As students progress from the initial problem to more general questions, they make predictions about expected relationships and give reasons for their ideas. Students identify patterns in their work and explain the significance of these patterns. They formulate other problems to test their insights and think about related situations.

Communication Throughout the lesson, students are encouraged to share ideas and create a dynamic problem-solving environment. Students engage in discussions that focus on inquiry rather than getting the right answer. They communicate their insights and understandings verbally and in writing.

Teaching Plan

Materials → Student pages 112–113

INTRODUCE THE LESSON BY PRESENTING a problem-solving situation for students to consider.

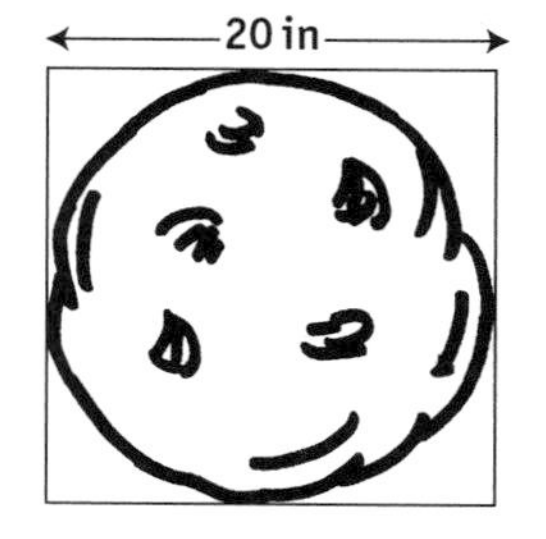

Ramon works at the Cookie Connection. The bakery's Monster Chip cookie is packaged in a box with a square bottom that measures 20 inches on a side. As Ramon looked at the cookie sitting in its box, he wondered what percent of the square bottom of the box the cookie covered.

Provide each student with a copy of student page 112 where they will find the situation represented. Emphasize that the cookie is a circle that exactly fits the box with the sides just touching. *What plan can be used to solve this problem?* Students should suggest these steps for finding a solution.

- Find the area of the square.
- Find the area of the circle.
- Form the ratio (*area of circle/area of square*) and express it as a percent.

Guide students through the steps to follow to solve the problem.

- *Do we have enough information to carry out each step?*
- *How will you find the area of the square?* (s^2; the length of a side is given.)
- *What is the area of the square?* (400 sq. in.; 20×20) Record this area next to the corresponding step on the board.
- *What do you need to know to find the area of the circle?* (The length of the radius)
- *What is the length of the radius? How can we find it?* (10 inches; Students should explain that the diameter of the circle is equal to the length of the side of the square, so the length of the radius is $20 \div 2 = 10$ in.)

Have students work individually or in pairs to find the area of the circle using 3.14 for π. ($A = 314$ sq. in.; 3.14×10^2) Then have them complete the problem by finding the percent. ($314 \div 400 = 0.785$; $0.785 \times 100 = 78.5\%$.)

Present a variation of the problem for students to consider.

> **Four Big Chip cookies fit in the same box as the Monster Chip. Ramon wonders what percent of the square bottom the 4 smaller cookies will cover.**

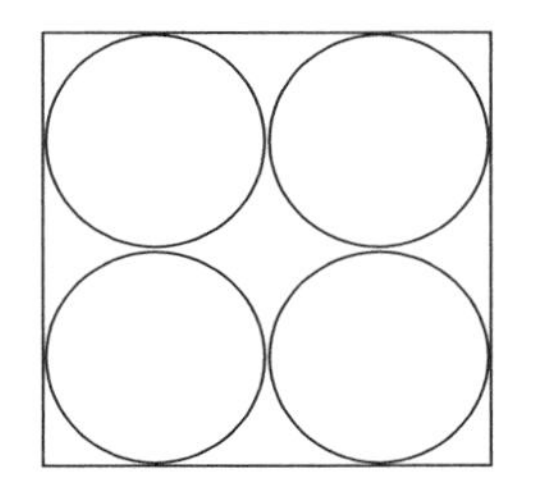

Invite students to predict how they think the percent of the square covered by the 4 cookies will compare with the answer they found for the Monster Chip and to explain their thinking. Encourage students to give their ideas until all three possibilities, less than, greater than, or equal to, have been expressed. Whether students' predictions are correct is not important since the results of the problem are counter-intuitive; the goal is to encourage students to engage in mathematical reasoning. Students may use imprecise terminology such as "little bits of area," but their arguments should reflect a logical structure.

Have students suggest a plan to solve the question. They should suggest finding the area of one small circle, multiplying that by 4 to get the total area, and then using the area of the square that they already know to compare the areas and express the comparison as a percent. Have students elaborate on how they will determine the length of the radius of the smaller circle. They should articulate that the diameter of each circle is half the side of the square and the radius is half of the diameter, or 5 in. *What is the total area covered by the cookies?* (314 sq. in.) At this point, observant students will note that since the total area is the same as for the Monster Cookie, they know the percent without any further computation—again, the answer is 78.5%.

Ask students if this result surprised them. *Based on these two problems, what question might occur to you?* Students may wonder if the area covered will always be 78.5% no matter how many circles are used. *What are the next two figures in this pattern?* (9 circles and 16 circles) Encourage students to investigate on their own. Instruct them to draw sketches. Using a calculator will facilitate computation. Students will find the circular areas continue to be 78.5% and they may find it interesting to speculate why.

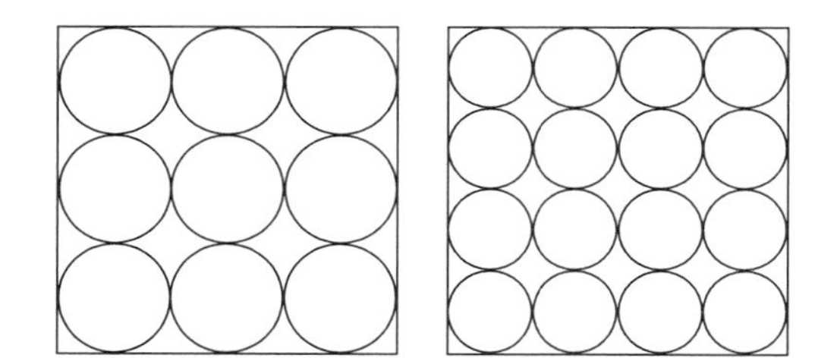

Prompt students to consider a related problem.

The square used in the above problems is 20 inches on a side. If the dimensions of the square were changed to, say 50 inches or 100 centimeters, would the percentage change?

Students could measure the areas again or they could use reasoning. Changing the dimensions would not change the ratio of radius to side length. The percent of the circular area would be the same; 78.5%.

Answers

Page 112

1. 400 in.^{2}; 314 in.^{2}; 78.5%
2. 400 in.^{2}; 314 in.^{2}; 78.5%
3. Square: A = 400 in.^{2}
   Circles: 9 circles; 314 in.^{2}; 78.5%; 16 circles; 314 in.^{2}; 78.5%;
4. Answers may vary. When any number of congruent circles are drawn (inscribed) inside a given square so that each circle touches the circle next to it and the sides of the circles touch the sides of the square, the area covered by the circles is always 78.5% of the area of the square.

Have students consider a different situation.

> **Suppose a square cake was packed, *inscribed*, in a circular tin of given diameter. What percent of the circular bottom would the cake cover?**

Although an analysis of this latter situation is beyond the students' skills at this time, the goal of the discussion is to have students recognize how problem solving in mathematics grows from one situation into many others. As students continue to learn about three-dimensional figures, they may formulate analogous packing problems using volumes.

If time allows, you may wish to have students begin work on some of the other problems on the student pages and discuss any questions that arise.

Student Pages

Student page 112 provides figures and recording space for the problems discussed during the lesson. Student page 113 includes additional problems involving measurements of circular regions and offers the students an opportunity to create their own problems.

Assessment

As students responded to questions and solved problems, it was possible to assess their ability to make a problem-solving plan and find needed information. As they worked, you were able to evaluate their proficiency at finding areas and carrying out other computations. The discussion about related problems provided an opportunity for you to note those students who could think creatively about mathematics.

NCTM Standards Summary

The problem-solving situations in this lesson served as a springboard for new questions. Students used reasoning to identify patterns for further investigation, to make predictions about expected results, and to justify their beliefs. They were encouraged to discuss alternate strategies and describe related problems that interested them. The approach of this lesson encouraged students to express their understandings and insights and helped them to recognize the ongoing nature of mathematical problem solving.

Answers

Page 113

1. 628 sq. mm
2. 4 in.
3. 16 in.^{2}
4. 4π
5. $\frac{1}{4}$ of the area
6. Subtract $4 \times \frac{1}{4}$ (area of cookie) from square.
7. $16 - 4\pi \approx 3.44$ in.^{2}
8. One method is to find area of square, find area of one whole circle (since $4 \times \frac{1}{4} = 1$); subtract to find good land, compare good land to area of square and determine if it is greater or less than half.
9. Area (square) = 10,000 sq. meters; Area (circle) = $1600\pi \approx$ 5,024 sq. meters; Swamp is greater by 48 sq. m.
10. Answers may vary.

Name

Using Circles

Solve each problem.

1. What percent of the square does a Monster Cookie cover? Assume the cookie is a circle.

   Area of square ____________

   Area of circle ____________

   Percent ____________

2. What percent of the square do the four smaller cookies cover?

   Area of square ____________

   Area of circle ____________

   Percent ____________

3. Draw the next two figures in the pattern. Find what percent of the square is covered by each.

   Area of square ____________

   Area of circle ____________

   Percent ____________

4. Write a statement summarizing your findings.

Name ______________________

Using Circles

Solve each problem. Use π = 3.14.

1. What is the area of the metal washer if the radius to the outer circle is 15 millimeters and the radius of the hole is 5 millimeters?

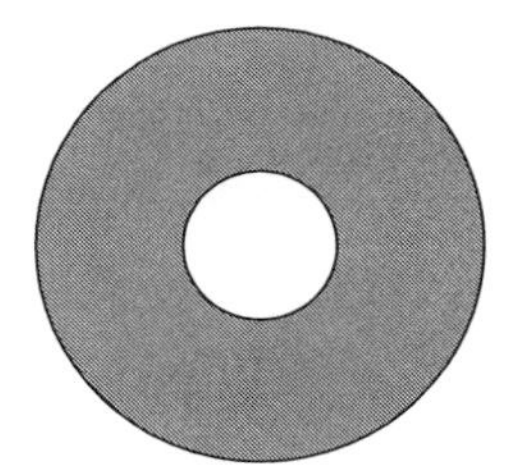

Four L'il Chip cookies are placed together as shown at the right. Draw a square that has one corner in the center of each cookie.

2. Find the length of the side of the square.
3. Find the area of the square.
4. Find the area of each cookie. Express your answer in terms of π.
5. What part of the area of each cookie is contained in the square you drew?
6. Explain the method you used.
7. What is the area of the shaded region?

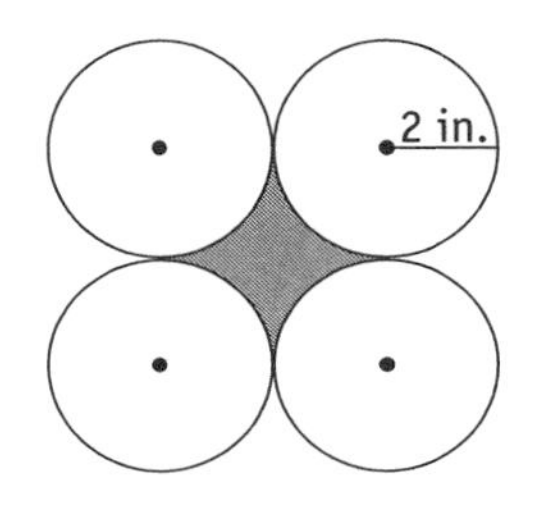

Mr. Coole bought the square piece of land shown. Unfortunately, he discovered the four shaded regions (four quarter circles) were swamps and not much good for anything.

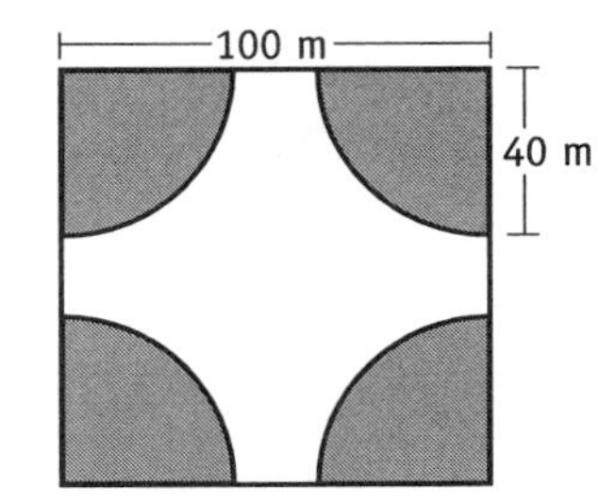

8. Which does he have more of—swamp or land? How much more?
9. Explain the steps you used to solve the problem and how you found the information you needed.
10. Create some problems suggested by the target shown.

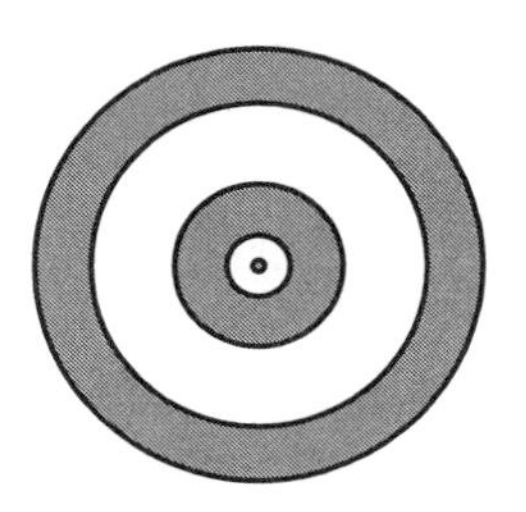

Converting Among Metric Units

Introduction

Objective → Students will be able to convert among metric units.

Context → This lesson ends a unit on dividing with decimals. Students are familiar with metric units and have estimated using metric units in the past.

Converting Among Metric Units

Learn

The metric system is based on 10. It is similar to our place-value system.

You can change from one unit to another by changing its place-value.

You multiply to change larger units to smaller units.
You divide to change smaller units to larger units.

$$\text{km} \underset{\div 1000}{\overset{\times 1{,}000}{\rightleftarrows}} \text{m} \underset{\div 100}{\overset{\times 100}{\rightleftarrows}} \text{cm} \underset{\div 10}{\overset{\times 10}{\rightleftarrows}} \text{mm}$$

Examples

Change 0.4 meters to centimeters.
1 m = 100 cm
$0.4 \times 100 = 40$
So, 0.4 m = 40 cm

Change 550 meters to kilometers.
1 km = 1,000 m
$550 \div 1{,}000 = 0.55$
So, 550 m = 0.55 km

More Examples

0.55 m = ■ cm
$0.55 \times 100 = 55$
0.55 m = 55 cm

2,300 mg = ■ g
$2{,}300 \div 1{,}000 = 2.3$
2,300 mg = 2.3 g

Try

1. Make diagrams like the one above to show how to change between milligrams (mg) and grams (g), and between grams and kilograms (kg).
2. Explain why you divide when changing from smaller units to larger units, and why you multiply when changing from larger units to smaller units.
3. 5.49 m = ■ cm
4. 1.3 kg = ■ mg
5. 0.2 km = ■ m
6. 5,000 mL = ■ L
7. 300 g = ■ kg
8. 4 cm = ■ mm

NCTM Process Standards Analysis and Focus

The standards analysis examines how the process standards have been incorporated into the above lesson. By increasing the focus on three of the process standards, a more effective and meaningful lesson can be presented. The suggestions offered can help you to think about how this might be accomplished.

Connections The lesson points out that changing metric units is similar to moving between place-value positions but does not develop that idea. A reference is made to the history and use of the metric system.

Suggestion → **Have students connect the metric prefixes with the decimal place-value system. Connect the ratios between the units to the steps for converting units. Emphasizing these**

Practice

Copy and complete the equations.

1. 1.8 kL = ■ L	**2.** 400 mg = ■ g	**3.** 2 g = ■ mg
4. 12.69 m = ■ cm	**5.** 2.3 km = ■ m	**6.** 6 kg = ■ g
7. 1,200 mg = ■ g	**8.** 4.5 cm = ■ mm	**9.** 50 mm = ■ cm
10. 6.4 km = ■ m	**11.** 25 mL = ■ L	**12.** 4,800 g = ■ kg
13. 12 mL = ■ L	**14.** 83,000 m = ■ k	**15.** 254 cm = ■ m

Compare the following by using $>$, $<$, or $=$.

17. 500 cm ■ 5 m	**18.** 0.03 m ■ 40 cm	**19.** 0.007 kg ■ 7 g
20. 2.5 kg ■ 2,500 mg	**21.** 26 kL ■ 3,345 L	**22.** 1.2 cm ■ 120 mm

Problem Solving

Solve the problem. Be prepared to explain your answer.

28. A building has 70 floors. Each of the first 5 floors is 7 m high. The rest of the floors are each 5 m high. How tall is the building? Express your answer in km.

29. An individual bottle of apple juice contains 180 mL of juice. A 12-pack contains 12 individual juice bottles. How many liters are in a 12-pack?

30. A 12-pack of apple juice costs $4.49. A liter size bottle costs $1.89. Which is cheaper per liter? Show how you arrived at your answer.

Communication

31. Write a problem that could be solved by changing meters to kilometers.

ideas will make the system of metric units more meaningful and give students a reference for comparing and renaming units. Expanding the historic background and real-life application of the metric system will bring added interest to this study.

Representation Labeled arrows that indicate multiplication when going from smaller to larger units and division when going from larger to smaller represent the method by which to rename units. Only the values for basic units, one hundredth of the basic units, and one thousand times the basic units are addressed in this lesson.

Suggestion → **All unit prefixes from millimeters through kilometers should be represented to help students understand the relationships between units. Placing metric prefixes along with decimal names into a place-value chart will help students remember their values and will provide a means for illustrating the steps for renaming units.**

Communication Communication is limited to supplying missing values; discussion would be discretionary. One question asking for an explanation could be used to generate discussion.

Suggestion → **Encourage discussion about the relationships between units. This will develop understanding and allow students to use relationships as they determine equivalence. Having students explain their thinking will prevent the errors that arise from rote use of conversion rules.**

Problem Solving Problem-solving exercises are actually word descriptions of situations that involve renaming units and arithmetic operations. Students are asked to write their own problem involving changing units.

Reasoning and Proof A question that asks students to explain why they multiply when changing to smaller units and divide when changing to larger units requires minimal reasoning.

The teaching plan that follows shows how the suggestions for increasing the focus on the process standards can be implemented.

Revised Teaching Plan

Materials → Meter sticks

BEGIN THE LESSON BY ASKING students to share information about the metric system. Discuss the history of the metric system, information about countries where the metric system is the standard measurement system, the status of the metric system in the United States, and the importance of the metric system in science and international business.

Review the basic metric units of length, mass, and volume, and help students identify a reference for each unit. *The average doorknob is about a meter above the floor. A meter is a little more than 3 feet. The thickness of a dime is a little less than a millimeter. A paper clip weighs about a gram. A liter is a little larger than a quart. Think of a liter-size bottle of soda.* Explain that what makes the metric system so easy to work with is that, unlike our standard or customary system, multiples or fractions of the basic unit always have the same relationship. For example, if you know it takes 100 centimeters to make a meter, then you will know it takes 100 centigrams to make a gram and 100 centiliters to make a liter. Compare this to 12 inches to a foot, 3 feet to a yard, 2 cups to a pint, 4 cups to a quart, and so on, where the ratio or exchange rate varies from one unit to the next. This discussion will make students more receptive to working with the metric system.

Draw the following place-value chart on the chalkboard.

thousands	hundreds	tens	ones	tenths	hundredths	thousandths
kilo-	*hecto-*	*deka-*	units (no prefix)	*deci-*	*centi-*	*milli-*
1,000	100	10	1	0.1	0.01	0.001
kilometer (km)	hectometer (hm)	dekameter (dem)	meter (m)	decimeter (dm)	centimeter (cm)	millimeter (mm)
1,000 m	100 m	10 m	1 m	0.1 m	0.01 m	0.001 m

FOCUS ON THE PREFIXES used in the metric system, from *milli-* to *kilo-*, and emphasize the connection between each prefix and its place-value meaning. Focusing on this relationship will help students understand the relative sizes of the units of measure without having to learn any new basic

f.y.i.

In 1866, by act of Congress, metric weights and measures were made lawful for all contracts, dealings, and court proceedings in the United States. In 1875, the Metric Convention was signed by 17 countries, including the United States, leading to internationally agreed-to metric standards that have served as the fundamental weights and measures standards of the United States. In 1971, the U.S. Secretary of Commerce recommended that the United States change to predominant use of the metric system through a coordinated program. Despite recommendations and efforts to change from the customary system, the metric system has still not become the system of choice for most Americans in daily use. All other major countries of the world use the metric system. [Adapted from Publication 304 A, 1972, U.S. Dept. of Commerce, National Bureau of Standards]

units. As you work through the prefixes, relate them to words students may know. For example, *centi-* is like cent, which is $\frac{1}{100}$ of a dollar; *deci-* is similar to decimal, which relates to tenths, and so on. Leave this information on the board for reference.

Use units of length to model working with the metric system. Display a meter stick to establish the basic unit of length. Ask students to identify reference points for the size of a meter. Consider having them measure where the meter mark falls on their bodies, and point out that while this measure is a good reference for now, it is subject to change as they continue to grow. Next, discuss the decimeter. Point out that for many people the width of their hand is about a decimeter. *Are decimeters bigger or smaller than meters?* (Smaller) *How many decimeters does it take to make a meter?* (10) *How many times larger than a decimeter is a meter?* (10 times larger) *What fraction of a meter is a decimeter?* ($\frac{1}{10}$ of a meter) These activities will help students understand the relationship between the two units and will give students handy personal references that are always available.

Discuss strategies for figuring out how to record the relationships between decimeters and meters. *If you have one decimeter and you want to write it in terms of meters, for example, 1 dm = __ m, would the number be larger or smaller? Why?* (Smaller, because one decimeter is smaller than one meter) *What part of a meter is a decimeter?* ($\frac{1}{10}$ or 0.1 m) Explain that when converting metric units, we always use the decimal form. Illustrate the relationship on the place-value chart, pointing to the "starting" unit (dm) and sliding your finger one place left to the "stop" unit (m). Explain how the direction of the move (left) and the number of moves (one) means the starting unit is $\frac{1}{10}$ of the ending unit and to divide by 10. Have students tell how to use the chart to write one millimeter in terms of meters. (Begin at mm, move three places left. Three places means $\frac{1}{10} \times \frac{1}{10} \times \frac{1}{10}$, or $\frac{1}{1,000}$, which means that the starting place is $\frac{1}{1,000}$ of the ending place. Conversely, the ending place is 1,000 times the starting place. Therefore, 1 mm = $\frac{1}{1000}$ m or 0.001 m.) Using the place-value chart offers visual reinforcement of the method for making the exchange and what it means.

Focus on changing larger units to smaller units. *How many decimeters are equal to one meter?* (10 dm = 1 m) *If you were changing 3 meters to decimeters, would the number get larger or smaller?* (Larger) *Why?* (Decimeters are smaller than meters. For every meter, you'd get

10 decimeters. It's like trading dollars for dimes.) *How many times bigger would the number get?* (10 times bigger) *So, if changing decimeters is 10 times as much, how many decimeters are equal to 3 meters?* (3 m = $3 \times 10 =$ 30 dm) Illustrate how going from meters to decimeters is one move right on the chart, which means multiply by 10. Give another example such as writing 24 meters as centimeters. With a discussion similar to that above, have students explain that since there are 100 centimeters to a meter, the number will be 100 times bigger, and $24 \times 100 = 2{,}400$. Then illustrate the place-value connection, having students explain how the number of places (two) and the direction (right) means to multiply by 100.

Help students generalize a rule by working though additional examples. *If you had* 15 *decimeters, would that be more or less than a meter?* (More) *Explain.* Students should be able to articulate that 10 decimeters make a meter, and 15 decimeters is more than that—in fact, it's $1\frac{1}{2}$ meters. Remind students that metric measures are expressed with decimals, and so 15 dm would be expressed as 1.5 dm.

Repeat these types of activities with different pairs of units, such as changing centimeters to decimeters, millimeters to decimeters, and so on. With each, emphasize how many there are of one unit to the other and whether the number will increase or decrease as the change is made. Illustrating on the place-value chart will help students generalize a method for changing from smaller to larger and larger to smaller units.

Discuss a few exchanges with units of mass (grams) and capacity (liters) to reinforce that the prefixes apply in the same way. Then go on to similar exercises with multiples of the basic unit, and include the prefixes *deka-*, *hecto-*, and *kilo-*.

Another way of looking at converting among metric units is to place decimal points in the place-value chart. Have students record the given number of a unit in the corresponding column(s) and place a decimal point immediately to the right of the unit to which they are converting. For example, if converting 4 decimeters to meters, the number 4 would be written in the decimeter column and a decimal point would go to the right of the meter's place. A zero placed in the meter column would show there are no meters. Any empty columns between the digits and decimal point should be filled with zeros. If students were exchanging 5 meters to centimeters, the 5 would go in the meter column, a decimal point would go to the right of the centimeter column, and the empty columns would be filled with zeros, showing 5 m = 500 cm.

thousands	hundreds	tens	ones	tenths	hundredths	thousandths
kilo-	*hecto-*	*deka-*	no prefix	*deci-*	*centi-*	*milli-*
1,000	100	10	1	0.1	0.01	0.001
kilometer	hectometer	dekameter	meter	decimeter	centimeter	millimeter
			0	4		
			5	0	0	

f.y.i.

Placing decimal points into the place-value chart provides a visual representation of the exchange method; however, caution should be exercised with its use lest it become a rote procedure. Emphasize the reasoning involved to promote understanding before introducing using decimal points in the place-value chart to students.

CONCLUDE THE LESSON by providing a few measurements and asking students to give equivalent values in several units. This will reinforce understanding of how the decimal point moves as units are renamed.

Student Pages

Students should now be ready to complete exercises similar to those on the reduced student pages.

Assessment

As students responded to questions during the class discussions, it was possible to determine their familiarity with basic metric units and the meaning of prefixes, as well as their understanding of the relationships among units. The conversion exercises at the end of the lesson provided an opportunity to assess students' fluency in exchanging among units.

NCTM Standards Summary

Emphasizing the connections between the metric system of measurement and the decimal place-value system helped students to understand the overall structure of the metric system and the relationships among the metric units. Representing metric prefixes along with decimal place values in charts provided visual reinforcement of how units are related and served as a memory aid. Using charts to represent the place-value relationships encouraged students to consider those relationships instead of resorting to rote manipulation of decimal points when making conversions. Finally, involving students in discussions that required reasoning about the relative sizes of units further enhanced their understanding of the conversion process.

Standard 5 **Data Analysis and Probability**

AT THE SIXTH GRADE LEVEL, data analysis and probability includes a lot of work with different graphical representations of data, collecting data, and probability concepts. Our lessons are derived from these important topics, and include a lesson on determining whether a game is fair or not, a lesson on planning and conducting a survey, a lesson on making and interpreting a circle graph, and a lesson on interpreting single- and double-line graphs.

Three lessons model how the process standards can be used to teach content. A fourth lesson is a hypothetical textbook lesson that we have revised to be more standards based. These four lessons do not represent the entire curriculum, but rather provide glimpses of how, with a more concentrated effort to incorporate the process standards, better mathematics teaching and learning can be achieved.

One lesson we have chosen has students determine whether or not certain games are fair. Through the process standards of reasoning and proof, communication, and connections, students support their conclusions for why a game is fair or unfair. They also are to figure out how to make an unfair game fair.

Another lesson we have chosen is one in which students plan and conduct a survey. Through the process standards of problem solving, communication, and reasoning and proof, students develop guidelines for creating a useful survey. This includes obtaining a fair sample, in terms of size and possible bias.

A third lesson is one on making and interpreting circle graphs. By incorporating the process standards, students develop a greater understanding of how to create and interpret circle graphs rather than just learning a step-by-step procedure. Through representation, communication, and connections, students realize just how many skills it takes to make and understand a circle graph.

The hypothetical textbook lesson that we have chosen to revise is a lesson in which students interpret information in both single- and double-line graphs. Through better incorporation of the process standards of representation, reasoning and proof, and communication, students are taught more about the usefulness of line graphs and are asked questions that require more thoughtfulness and interpretation, rather than ones requiring isolated bits of information.

Standard 5 Lessons

Playing Fair

Planning and Conducting Surveys

Making and Interpreting Circle Graphs

Interpreting Single- and Double-Line Graphs

Playing Fair

Introduction

Objective → Students will determine whether games are fair and will identify the probability of winning.

Context → This lesson comes late in a unit that includes probability. Students have had prior experience with rational numbers, decimals, percents, and basic probability concepts. Students may go on to learn about compound events and counting techniques.

NCTM Standards Focus

In this standards-based approach to exploring probability, students will examine games to determine whether they are fair. They will connect their knowledge of ratios and fractions to procedures used in finding the probability of events. Reasoning will be employed to revise unfair games in order to make them fair, and students will create rules for fair and unfair games of their own design. Discussion about the probability of outcomes in the various situations they examine will help students clarify and reinforce their understanding of the concepts being developed.

Reasoning and Proof Reasoning and proof is a key element in this lesson as students determine whether game situations are fair and give reasons to justify their answers. Reasoning is also key in figuring out how to alter unfair games to make them fair and in designing probability games.

Communication Through class discussion, students share their ideas about fairness in general and each game in particular. By explaining their opinions about different games to one another, students clarify their own thinking about fairness and the likelihood of outcomes, and gain experience in formulating convincing mathematical arguments.

Connections In order to determine the possible outcomes for a game, students rely on prior knowledge involving number operations, ratios, and operations with fractions. Since playing games is part of the students' everyday experience, the lesson has a natural real-life connection.

Teaching Plan

Materials → Student pages 126–127; spinners; number cubes; a deck of standard playing cards; coins (optional)

INTRODUCE THE LESSON by asking students to consider fairness in games. *When is a game fair? When is a game unfair?* Most students will be able to explain that a game is fair when each player has an equal chance of winning. A game is unfair when one or more players have a greater chance of winning than other players do. *How can you determine the chances of winning in a game?* Explain that by determining the probability of the outcomes that are possible, students will be able to determine the chances of winning in many types of games.

Briefly review basic probability concepts in the context of the familiar situation of tossing a coin. *If you toss a fair coin, how many outcomes are possible?* (Two) *What are they?* (Heads or tails) *What is the probability that heads will be the result of a single toss of the coin? Explain.* ($\frac{1}{2}$; heads is one of the two possible outcomes.) *Suppose you and a friend play a game in which you call heads or tails, and the result of a coin toss determines the winner. Is this game fair? Why?* (Yes. On any given toss, each player has the same chance of having the coin come up with his/her call.)

Present a second situation for students to consider.

> **Suppose you are playing a game in which you toss two fair coins. If both coins come up heads, you win. If both coins come up tails, your opponent wins.**

What outcomes are possible when two coins are tossed? (HH, HT, TH, TT) Write the outcomes on the board. *What is the probability you will win?* ($\frac{1}{4}$) *What is the probability your opponent will win?* ($\frac{1}{4}$) *What is the probability nobody will win?* ($\frac{2}{4}$, or $\frac{1}{2}$) *Is this game fair? Explain.* (Yes. Each player has the same chance of winning.) *How could you change the rules of this game so that it will still be fair but you and your opponent will each have a better chance of winning?* (One possibility is to have you win if both coins show heads or both show tails, and to have your opponent win if one coin is a head and one is a tail. That way each player has two favorable out of four possible outcomes, or a $\frac{1}{2}$ probability of winning.)

Present another situation to the class.

> **Suppose you play a game in which a fair number cube is tossed. You win if a number less than 3 shows; otherwise your opponent wins.**

What outcomes are possible when you toss a number cube? (1, 2, 3, 4, 5, and 6.) *Is the game described a fair game? Explain.* (No. Since only 1 and 2 are less than 3, your chances are 2 out of 6, or $\frac{1}{3}$. Your opponent's chances are 4 out of 6, or $\frac{2}{3}$.) *How can you change the game to make it fair?* (You win on 3 or less; otherwise, your opponent wins.)

> **Suppose two fair number cubes are tossed, and the sum of the numbers is formed. You win if the sum is 6, the second player wins if the sum is 7, and the third player wins if the sum is 8. Otherwise, nobody wins.**

f.y.i.

Probability is the ratio of the number of favorable outcomes to the number of possible outcomes, given that each favorable and unfavorable outcome is equally likely to occur. For example, when tossing a coin, the coin must be a fair one; it must have both heads and tails and cannot be weighted to land on only one side.

Is this a fair game? If not, which player has an advantage? (The game is not fair; the second player, who wins with a sum of 7, has an advantage.) Discuss the possible outcomes and draw a table on the board to show all 36 sums and how they are formed. Then examine the number of favorable outcomes for each player. Students should explain that the probability of getting a sum of 6 is $\frac{5}{36}$; a sum of 7 is $\frac{6}{36}$, or $\frac{1}{6}$; and a sum of 8 is $\frac{5}{36}$.

add	1	2	3	4	5	6
1	1 + 1 = 2	1 + 2 = 3	1 + 3 = 4	1 + 4 = 5	1 + 5 = 6	1 + 6 = 7
2	2 + 1 = 3	2 + 2 = 4	2 + 3 = 5	2 + 4 = 6	2 + 5 = 7	2 + 6 = 8
3	3 + 1 = 4	3 + 2 = 5	3 + 3 = 6	3 + 4 = 7	3 + 5 = 8	3 + 6 = 9
4	4 + 1 = 5	4 + 2 = 6	4 + 3 = 7	4 + 4 = 8	4 + 5 = 9	4 + 6 = 10
5	5 + 1 = 6	5 + 2 = 7	5 + 3 = 8	5 + 4 = 9	5 + 5 = 10	5 + 6 = 11
6	6 + 1 = 7	6 + 2 = 8	6 + 3 = 9	6 + 4 = 10	6 + 5 = 11	6 + 6 = 12

Can you find a way of making this game fair? (One way: first player 2 or 6, second player 7, third player 8 or 12, so that each player's probability is $\frac{1}{6}$. Another way: first player 4, 5, or 6, second player 8, 9, or 10, third player 2, 3, 7, 11, 12. This solution makes each player's probability of winning $\frac{1}{3}$. Other solutions are possible.) The reasoning students are required to use in these exercises will reinforce their understanding of fairness and probability.

DISTRIBUTE STUDENT PAGE 126. Have students work individually or in pairs to create rules for two games. Tell them to make one game fair and the other game unfair. Instruct students to color the sections in each of the spinners and to write the rules for each game in the spaces provided. Tell them to indicate the probability of winning for each player, to indicate whether the game is fair or unfair, and to explain why.

Have students present and compare their games. As a class, students should agree whether or not each game described is fair or unfair. If time allows, students may propose other spinner games in which the sections are numbered instead of colored.

Extension

Have students work individually or in pairs to create fair and unfair variations of games. They may use number cubes, cards, spinners, coins, or counters. Have them present each version, and ask the class to decide if it is fair or unfair.

Student Pages

Student page 126 provides spinner diagrams and recording space for student-created games. Student page 127 offers practice exercises involving fair and unfair games.

Assessment

Their responses regarding the fairness of games that were described indicated students' understanding of probability concepts. It was possible to assess students' ability to reason through these concepts by evaluating the games they created.

NCTM Standards Summary

As they analyzed increasingly complex games and determined whether they were fair, students developed skill in identifying outcomes and probabilities. Students reasoned to find ways to revise unfair games, affirming their comprehension of the lesson concepts. Explaining how unfair games could be altered to make them fair allowed students an opportunity to clarify and reinforce their understanding of probability. Connections were made to knowledge of ratios, number operations, and fractions as outcomes were determined, while the context of games provided a meaningful and interesting connection to students' real-life experiences.

Answers

Page 126

Answers will vary.

Page 127

1. Unfair; $P(\text{picture card}) = \frac{3}{13}$, $P(\text{non-picture card}) = \frac{10}{13}$
2. Unfair; $P(\text{A–L}) = \frac{6}{13}$, $P(\text{M–Z}) = \frac{7}{13}$
3. Fair; $P(\text{odd}) = \frac{1}{2}$, $P(\text{even}) = \frac{1}{2}$
4. Fair; $P(\text{prime}) = \frac{1}{2}$; $P(\text{not prime}) = \frac{1}{2}$
5.

×	1	2	3	4	5	6
1	1	2	3	4	5	6
2	2	4	6	8	10	12
3	3	6	9	12	15	18
4	4	8	12	16	20	24
5	5	10	15	20	25	30
6	6	12	18	24	30	36

6. 36
7. Unfair; $P(\geq 20) = \frac{2}{9}$, $P(<20) = \frac{7}{9}$

8–9. Answers will vary.

Name

Playing Fair

Create a probability game for each spinner. Make one game fair and the other unfair. Color the sections of the spinners. Write rules to tell how to play each game and include the number of players. Tell each player's probability of winning, whether the game is fair or unfair, and why.

Game 1

Rules

Probabilities

Fair/Unfair

Game 2

Rules

Probabilities

Fair/Unfair

Name

Playing Fair

Tell whether each game is fair or unfair. Give reasons to support each answer.

1. Pick one card from a standard deck of 52. You win a point if a picture card is selected. Otherwise, your opponent wins a point.

2. Pick a card from a set containing the letters of the alphabet. You win if the card is any letter from A to L. Your opponent wins if the card is any letter from M to Z.

3. Use the spinner shown at the right. If the outcome is an odd number, you win. Your opponent wins if the outcome is even.

4. Spin the spinner shown at the right. You win if the outcome is a prime number. Otherwise, your opponent wins.

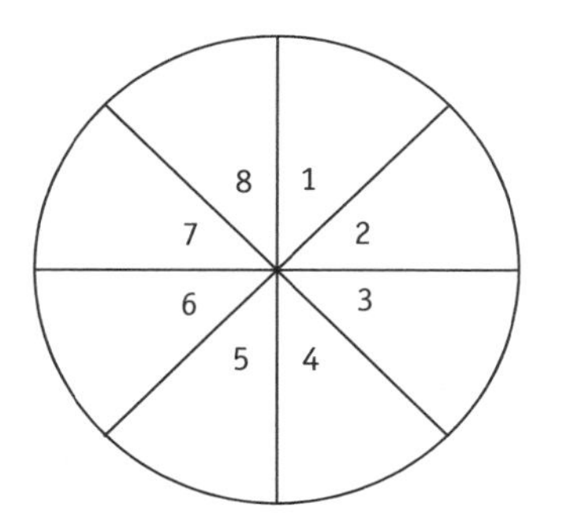

Complete the following questions, based on multiplying the numbers on two fair number cubes.

5. Fill in the table to show all the possible products than can be formed.

6. How many possible outcomes are there?

×	1	2	3	4	5	6
1						
2						
3						
4						
5						
6						

7. Suppose you win if the product is 20 or more; otherwise your opponent wins. Is this game fair? Explain.

8. Create a fair game based on the products in the table. Explain why the game is fair.

9. Create an unfair game based on the products in the table. Explain why the game is unfair.

Planning and Conducting Surveys

Introduction

Objective → Students will understand issues involved in conducting fair surveys, including sample size and bias, and will be able to apply information to create and conduct surveys of their own.

Context → This lesson comes early in a unit that deals with displaying and analyzing data. Students have worked with fractions, decimals, and percents. They will go on to learn about specialized methods for displaying data, such as stem and leaf plots and measures of central tendency.

NCTM Standards Focus

In this standards-based lesson, reasoning and communication become important in helping students understand how surveys can be used to gather information. By examining and discussing various survey situations, students learn to evaluate the features that must be present for the results of a survey to be valid. They focus on the importance of clear and objective expression as they examine questioning techniques and become aware of the care that must be taken in constructing and reporting surveys. Finally, students choose their own survey topic and create their own survey plans.

Problem Solving Students explore surveys as the means for gathering information to solve certain problems. By considering different situations, they develop guidelines that must be followed for the survey results to be useful. They then plan and conduct a survey to gather information about a subject of their own choosing.

Communication Communication is a major focus of this lesson. Students discuss the issues that must be considered in planning an effective survey, including the form of communication used with survey participants. Students develop an understanding of the need for clarity of expression as they evaluate the content of survey questions.

Reasoning and Proof Students use reasoning as they examine surveying techniques to find flaws. They justify their own survey plans based on their understanding of a fair sample. Through these activities, students gain experience meeting the standards of statistical investigation.

Teaching Plan

Materials → Student pages 132–133

BEGIN THE LESSON with a discussion to introduce lesson vocabulary. *How many of you are familiar with surveys? What is a survey?* (A method of gathering data by asking questions) Explain that another term often used for *survey* is *poll*. Ask students to provide examples of surveys they know about and tell why they are taken. (Examples might include predicting election results, determining consumer preferences, drawing conclusions about conditions such as employment, job satisfaction, and so on.)

Explain that surveys are about the views of an entire interest group or *population*. For example, with a survey about the musical tastes of 6th graders, the *population* might be all of the 6th graders in a particular school, town, state, or, in the U.S. *What difficulties might be encountered while trying to survey an entire population?* (It can be very costly and take a long time.) Explain that rather than survey an entire population, generally a *sample*, a part of the larger population, is surveyed. *What are some of the things to think about when selecting a sample to survey about an issue?* (Is the sample size large enough? Does the sample represent the whole population?) *When might the survey process be unfair, or biased?* (When too many people with a particular interest or characteristic are included, or when the questions are asked in a way that influences the answers)

f.y.i.

Students may be interested to know that there are mathematical techniques that can be used to determine appropriate sample sizes.

How could you find out the favorite afterschool snack among the students in a school with a population of 500 *students?* Your students should realize that either written or oral surveys would be required. Present the following strategies for gathering information and discuss the merits of each.

- **Survey 10% of the students.**
  How many students would be questioned? (50) *Do you think this sample is large enough?* (Maybe. It could be larger.) *Why?* (It might not fairly represent whole school.) *How would the 10% be selected?* (Not indicated, but this is an important consideration)
- **Select 10 students at random from each classroom.**
  Assuming there are 20 classrooms (5 classes each of grades 5 through 8), how many students would be involved in the survey? (200) *Is this a good sample size?* (Yes. It may even be too large.) *Is this a good sampling strategy? Why?* (It is good since students are chosen by chance. However, students who are absent would not have an opportunity to be chosen.) *How could the strategy be improved?* (Choose students from the class list. If a student chosen is absent, contact him/her by telephone.)
- **Question the first 100 students to arrive at school one morning.**
  Is this a good plan? (The sample size is appropriate. Using the first 100 students is convenient, but may not provide a representative overview of the school population; what if all 100 students are eighth graders because that grade starts first? Their preferences may be different from those of other students.)

- **Survey 50 students at afterschool sports practice.**
  Is this OK? (Using only athletes may result in bias; they may be different from the students as a whole.)
- **Send a printed questionnaire to all students in the school and tally the results from the first 75 responses.**
  Is this a good plan? (Students who respond may have strong opinions and thus be motivated to reply; less interested students would not be included.) *How could the plan be improved?* (Pick 75 students at random, send a questionnaire, then follow up if student does not reply.)

After each of the situations above has been discussed, reinforce the key points about conducting a survey and selecting a sample. *Why is the size of the sample important?* (The sample must be large enough to convey the real opinions of all those who could have been surveyed. If, for example, only 10 students were questioned, it is unlikely the sample would represent the characteristics, such as male/female ratio, age distribution, ethnic balance, etc., of the entire population of 500.) *Why is using a random selection method good?* (Random selection avoids samples with a particular characteristic or association.) Emphasize that if the results of a survey are biased, they are invalid because they do not accurately represent their stated purpose.

INVOLVE STUDENTS IN A DISCUSSION about survey methods (paper-and-pencil survey, telephone call, face-to-face contact) and the wording of questions. Students should be aware that in some surveys, people may respond differently when face-to-face with an interviewer or when filling out a questionnaire that includes their name. For example, a student may not want to admit that his or her favorite snack is something other students may think is strange. Questions that include a list—for example, pizza, ice cream, hamburgers, and cookies—focus the responses but they also limit and influence them.

Encourage students to share relevant ideas and comments on the advantages and disadvantages of different survey methods and question structures. Emphasize that questions should be designed in a way that does not influence the response. Have them suggest appropriate types of questions and questioning techniques about student satisfaction with the cafeteria.

- Inappropriate: Do you think the food in the cafeteria is terrible?
- Appropriate: How would you rate the food in the cafeteria?

Answers

Page 132

1. A method of collecting statistical data in which people are asked to answer questions
2. Questioning or canvassing people at random to obtain information or opinions to be analyzed; survey
3. The universal set from which a sample of statistical data is selected
4. A finite subset of a population used for statistical analysis
5. Survey in which the sample does not fairly represent the population and/or questions influence responses
6. Survey in which the sample fairly represents the population and questions elicit unbiased responses

CONCLUDE THE LESSON with a brief discussion of how survey results can be analyzed and reported. Have students consider the survey on favorite foods discussed earlier. *How might the results of the survey influence which items would be reported?* (If the top two or three were very close in votes, it would make sense to report them; if one item was way ahead of all others, then it alone might be reported.) Point out that in summarizing the results of a survey, it is desirable to state the important features such as size of the sample, where and when the survey was conducted, method of contact, and so on. Emphasize that students should evaluate surveys they read or hear about with regard to these features.

Student Pages

Student page 132 provides a review of lesson vocabulary and practice exercises involving survey planning. Student page 133 outlines the steps students can use to conduct a survey.

Assessment

Students' responses to the questions about survey design during the class discussion provided opportunities to assess understanding of the features that make a good survey. Reviewing answers to questions, plans, and results for the survey activity outlined on the student pages, helped you to judge individual and cooperative application of the lesson principles.

NCTM Standards Summary

In this lesson, problem solving and reasoning worked together as students explored how surveys are used to gather information. Students discussed surveys as a means of gathering information for decision making, and examined the features that must be present for a survey to be useful. There were opportunities to discuss and evaluate different survey situations, which enabled students to share their thinking and be exposed to a broad range of ideas. The communication aspects of surveys themselves were considered, making students aware of the importance of clear and objective expression. As students used reasoning to evaluate survey plans, they were alerted to the care that must be taken in constructing and reporting surveys. Finally, by creating and justifying their own survey plans, students developed greater insight into the set of criteria that characterizes a good survey.

7. Advantage—random
   Disadvantage—might not represent population
8. Advantage—convenient
   Disadvantage—too small a sample; not representative of population
9. Advantage—convenient; are sneaker wearers
   Disadvantage—might be influenced by sport, coach, or favorite athlete
10. Advantage—random; likely to give large sample
    Disadvantage—eliminates people not wearing sneakers
11. Advantage—convenient
    Disadvantage—might not be representative of population
12. Advantage—convenient
    Disadvantage—too small a sample; not likely to be representative of population
13. Advantage—random; likely to be large enough sample
    Disadvantage—might not answer phone; might not cooperate with telephone surveys
14. Advantage—convenient
    Disadvantage—might not be seen; only people interested in responding will do so

Page 133
Answers will vary.

Name

Planning and Conducting Surveys

Explain each of the following terms in your own words.

1. survey
2. poll
3. population
4. sample
5. biased survey
6. unbiased survey

Suppose you want to determine the most popular brand of sneakers. Explain the advantages and disadvantages of choosing a sample in each of the following ways.

7. Ask every tenth person who enters a nearby shoe store.
8. Ask ten of your friends.
9. Ask ten members of the school basketball team.
10. Ask every person wearing sneakers in your school on a particular day.

Suppose you want to determine what percent of adults in your community would attend a weekend performance of a school play. Explain the advantages and disadvantages of choosing a sample in each of the following ways.

11. Ask 50 adults who shop at the local supermarket on Saturday morning.
12. Select some streets in the community at random, and ask the first five adults you meet on each street.
13. Pick the first name at the top of each column of the local telephone directory and call that person.
14. Leave questionnaires at popular local stores with a sign asking people to fill them out and drop them in a box you make available.

Name

Planning and Conducting Surveys

Conduct your own survey. Work alone or with a group of classmates.

Select a subject whose popularity you would like to know more about. Also think about how the results of your survey could be used.

Write a question about the subject you chose. Decide if you will use a *yes/no* question, an *agree/disagree* question, or one that requires the person responding to choose his or her own answer. Test your question on several people. If the question is misunderstood, change it.

Decide on the population you will sample. Describe the population.

Determine the size of your sample. (Remember that you are actually going to conduct this survey.) How many people will you question?

Describe the method you will use to choose your sample.

Explain how you will contact the participants and ask them the question.

Explain how you will record your data.

Conduct your survey. (Obtain any special permission from your teacher that might be necessary.)

Analyze your data.

Write a brief report in which you describe the reason for your survey, how it was conducted, and the results you obtained.

Making and Interpreting Circle Graphs

Introduction

Objective → Students will construct a circle graph from data organized in a table and will interpret information in the completed graph.

Context → This lesson comes toward the end of a unit on ratio, proportion, and percent. Students have practiced basic percent skills and are familiar with angle measurement and angle relationships in geometric figures. Students may go on to learn more about statistics, graphing, and probability.

NCTM Standards Focus

Through the incorporation of the process standards, this lesson, in which students create and interpret circle graphs, becomes a meaningful learning experience rather than a series of rote steps to follow. Students discuss the steps for constructing circle graphs, making connections to several areas of mathematics, including fractions, percents, and geometry. Finally, students answer specific questions requiring them to interpret the information represented in circle graphs.

Representation Students convert data from tabular form to visual representation by creating a circle graph. They consider the advantages of the visual representation and the types of data for which this representation method is appropriate.

Communication Students examine part/whole relationships of a set of data and discuss how those relationships can be accurately represented in circle graphs. This procedure helps them recognize the purpose of each step required in creating the graph. By sharing ideas, students gain greater insight into interpreting circle graphs.

Connections Throughout the lesson, students make connections to other areas of their mathematical knowledge, reinforcing how different mathematical concepts can be used to build new knowledge. They compare and contrast types of graphs and they apply computational skills and geometric understanding in the creation of a circle graph.

Teaching Plan

Materials → Student pages 138–139; blank circles marked with center dot; protractors; examples of circle graphs

BEGIN THE LESSON by asking students to recall circle graphs they have seen and to describe their purposes. Students' responses should reflect an understanding that circle graphs are used to compare parts of a whole. Display a few circle graphs and have students discuss comparisons that can be made with each.

Present the following data from a survey about methods of transportation to school:

24 students walk, 18 bicycle, 66 ride the school bus, and 12 are driven

Have students work independently to organize the data into a table. After reviewing the tabular data, ask students to consider other ways to display the information. *Would you present this data as a bar graph?* (Yes.) *As a pictograph?* (Yes.) *How about as a line graph?* (No.) *Why not?* (Line graphs show changes or trends over time and, therefore, would not be suitable as a way to display this set of data.) *What advantage would be gained by representing this data as a circle graph rather than as a bar graph, a pictograph, or even a table?* (A circle graph makes it easy to see the relationship of the categories to each other, as well as the relationship of each category to the whole. It shows relationships at a glance.) This discussion will help students recognize that different types of graphs serve different purposes.

ENGAGE STUDENTS IN A DISCUSSION about the steps needed for converting the tabular data about methods of transportation into a circle graph. *How many students were included in the transportation survey?* (120) *How do you know?* (Add.) *How can you determine what percentage of the total each category represents?* (Students may suggest different methods.)

Methods Students Might Suggest

- Write each category as a fraction, then write the fraction as a percent.
- Express each category as a decimal, then as a percent.
- Use proportions such as $\frac{24}{120} = \frac{n}{100}$ and solve for n.

Have students work individually or in pairs to determine the percentage for each category. You may wish to have students use calculators. Ask students to explain how they can check to be sure their computations are correct. They should understand that the sum of the percents for each category should be 100%. Having students check their computations will reinforce the part/whole relationships they are working with.

NEXT, HAVE STUDENTS CONSIDER how each method of transportation can be represented as a part of a circle. Point out that each part or sector of the circle is determined by the measure of the angle formed by two radii. *How many degrees are there in circle?* (360°) *How can the percentage for each transportation method be used to determine the number of degrees required for its sector of the circle?* (Find the percent of 360.) By developing the steps through their own reasoning, and then carrying them out, students will gain a much better understanding of the process.

Have students work in pairs to complete the following expanded version of the data table. *(Note: Answers to be filled in are in parentheses.)*

Methods of Transportation to School

Method	Number	Percent of Total	Number of Degrees in Sector
Walk	24	(20%)	(72°)
Bicycle	18	(15%)	(54°)
School Bus	66	(55%)	(198°)
Driven	12	(10%)	(36°)
Totals	**120**	**(100%)**	**(360°)**

Ask students to explain how they can check to see that they have computed the measures of the sectors correctly. They should understand that the sum of the angles must equal 360°, the number of degrees in a circle.

Provide the students with a circle marked with a center dot. Instruct students to work with their partners to create the circle graph by using a protractor to measure and draw the correct angle for each sector.

What Might Happen . . . What to Do

Some students may have difficulty working with the protractor and creating the sectors. Suggest that students begin by drawing a radius and then measuring from this line. Circulate among the groups and offer help as needed.

Remind students to label each sector of the graph and suggest they use different colors for emphasis. When students finish labeling, pose questions to guide them in interpreting their circle graphs. *What does the largest sector of the graph represent?* (bus; the most used method) *the smallest?* (driven; least used method) *Why is it easier to compare the data represented in a circle graph than within a table?* (Relationships can be seen at a glance.) *When is the table more useful?* (When you need to work with numbers of students rather than percents)

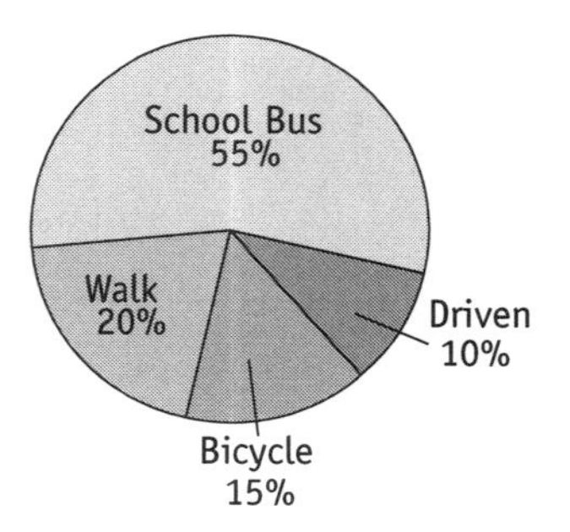

Answers

Page 138
Cereal Sales for One Week
Corny Crisps: 38%, 137°
Branny Bits: 30%, 108°
Wonder Wheat: 18%, 65°
Great Oats: 9%, 32°
Sweet Morning: 5%, 18°
Total: 100%, 360°
(Note: Degrees have been rounded.)

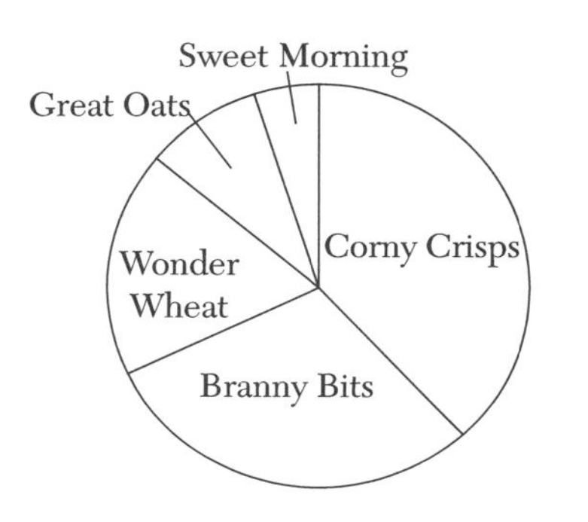

Pet Ownership
0: 12%, 43°
1: 41%, 148°
2: 34%, 122°
3: 9%, 32°
4: 3%, 11°
More than 4: 1%, 4°
Total: 100%, 360°
(Note: Percentages and degrees have been rounded.)

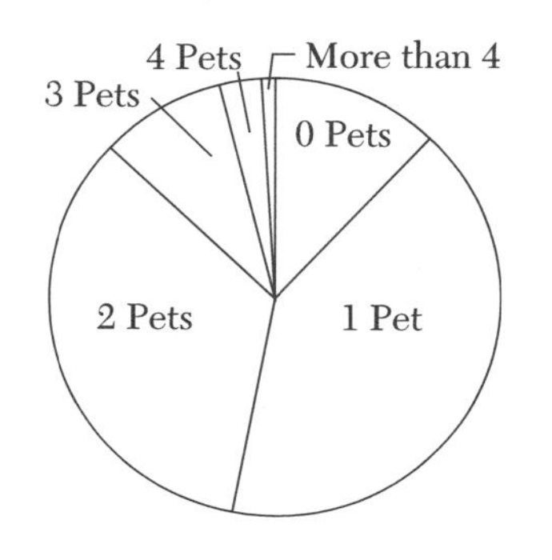

If time allows, survey the methods of transportation used by the class to get to school and represent the data in a circle graph. This may provide an opportunity to discuss the use of rounding of percents and angle measures, and the slight discrepancies that may result in the totals. *How does our class graph compare to the one we just completed? How is it different? Which transportation method does our class use most frequently? How many different methods does our class use?* It may be appropriate to discuss the use of an "Other" category to simplify the graphing process.

Student Pages

Student page 138 gives practice in the steps needed to construct circle graphs from given data. Student page 139 provides additional practice in constructing a circle graph plus practice with interpreting a circle graph.

Assessment

Student responses during class discussion could be used to assess understanding of the purposes of different graphs and the basic relationships in a circle graph. The completed table and circle graph served as indicators of student fluency with computations and the graph construction process.

NCTM Standards Summary

In this lesson, students had the opportunity to consider the advantages and appropriateness of different forms of data displays. By comparing different graphic forms of representing data, they could recognize how the visual representation of circle graphs showed relationships at a glance. Communication of ideas enabled students to develop the steps for constructing a circle graph based on their own understanding of the features of the graph. In completing the graphs, students made connections to several areas of mathematics and gained insight into the complementary structure that exists among the different areas. Finally, discussion of the data and how the graphs could be interpreted made the lesson more interesting and provided a link to real-world situations.

Answers

Page 139

March Expenses for Robert's Family
- Housing: 35%, 126°
- Food: 23%, 83°
- Clothing: 8%, 29°
- Transportation: 7%, 25°
- Health Care: 18%, 65°
- Entertainment: 5%, 18°
- Personal Grooming: 4%, 14°
- Miscellaneous: 1%, 4°
- Total: 100%, 360°
- *(Note: Percentages and degrees have been adjusted.)*

1. Plants, 56%
2. 20%; Fishes 8% + Birds 12%
3. Reptiles, Amphibians 4% + Insects, Arachnids 3% = Mammals 7%
4. Plants; Plants represent 56%, which is more than half.
5. 75 species; Snails, Clams, Crustaceans are 10% of 750 species, so multiply 10% × 750.

Making and Interpreting Circle Graphs

Complete each table. Then create a circle graph for each set of data.

Cereal Sales for One Week

Bread	Number of Boxes	Percent of Total	Number of Degrees in Sector
Corny Crisps	76		
Branny Bits	60		
Wonder Wheat	36		
Great Oats	18		
Sweet Morning	10		
Totals			

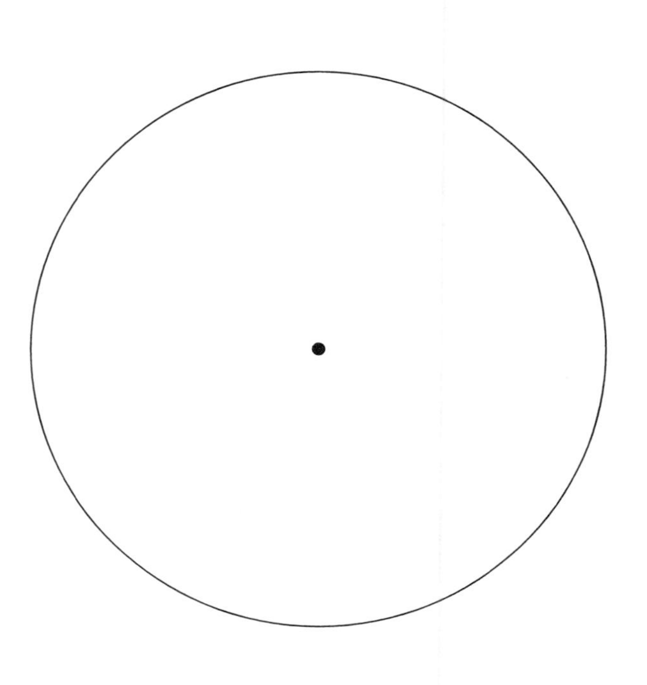

Pet Ownership

Number of Pets	Number of Owners	Percent of Total	Number of Degrees in Sector
0	62		
1	205		
2	170		
3	43		
4	15		
More than 4	5		
Total			

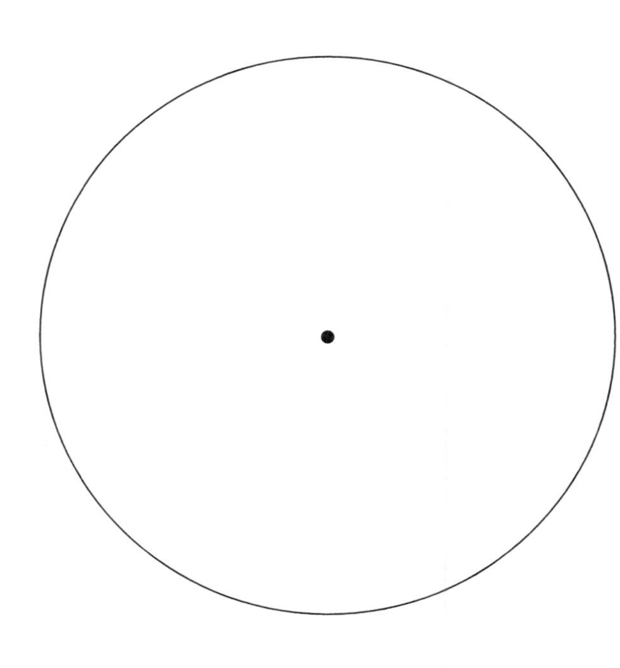

Name

Making and Interpreting Circle Graphs

Complete the table. Then create a circle graph for the set of data.

March Expenses for Robert's Family

Type of Expense	Amount	Percent of Total	Number of Degrees in Sector
Housing	$1,020		
Food	660		
Clothing	225		
Transportation	204		
Health Care	512		
Entertainment	137		
Personal Grooming	103		
Miscellaneous	39		
Total			

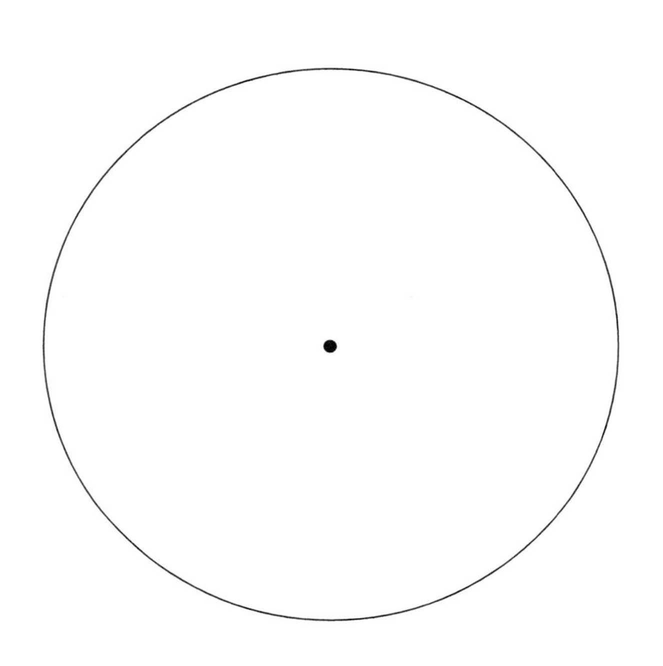

Answer each question.

1. Which category has the most endangered species?
2. What percent of endangered species are either fishes or birds?
3. Which two groups combined represent about the same number of endangered species as mammals?
4. Are there more species of plants or animals (non-plants) that are endangered? Explain how you arrived at your conclusion.
5. If the total number of endangered species in the U.S. is 750, about how many species are in the group *Snails, Clams, Crustaceans?* Explain how you found your answer.

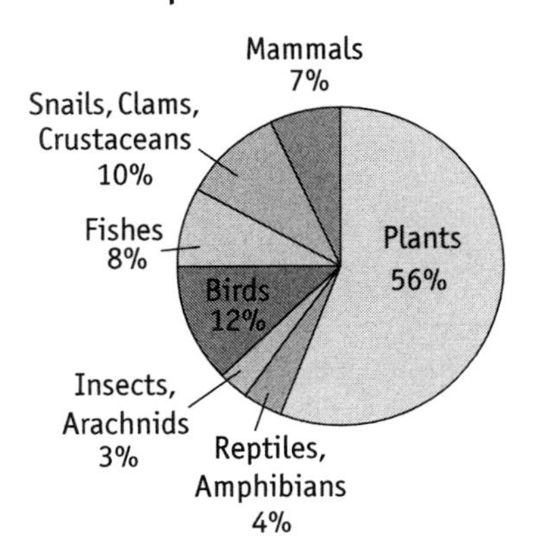

Interpreting Single- and Double-Line Graphs

Introduction

Objective → Students will interpret single- and double-line graphs.

Context → This lesson appears early in a unit on data analysis. Students have studied operations with decimals. They have just completed work with bar graphs and will continue to work with graphing before going on to study probability.

Intrepreting Single- and Double-Line Graphs

Learn

Antoine lives in Hartford, Connecticut. He has a friend who moved to Portland, Oregon. Antoine's friend says it seems to rain a lot more in Portland than in Hartford. Antoine wants to know if this is true, so he made a double line graph with the data he collected.

Average Monthly Precipitation (inches)

Month	Portland	Hartford
January	6.0	3.5
February	4.0	3.5
March	3.5	4.0
April	2.5	4.0
May	2.0	3.5
June	1.5	3.5
July	0.5	3.0
August	1.0	4.0
September	1.5	4.0
October	3.0	3.5
November	5.5	4.0
December	6.5	4.0

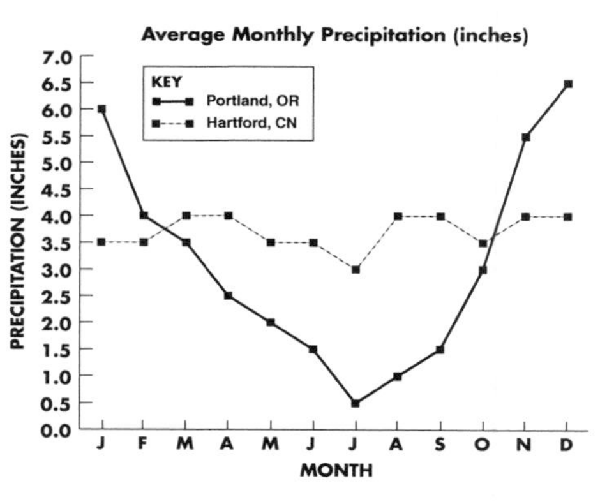

The two figures above show the same data. One has the data in the form of a table, the other has the data in the form of a graph. The table is a collection of data, while the graph is a picture of the **trend** of the data. Answer the following questions. Tell whether it is easier to find the answer using the table or the graph.

1. What is the average precipitation for October in Portland? In Hartford?
2. Which month has the greatest amount of precipitation in Portland? In Hartford?
3. Which month has the least amount of precipitation in Portland? In Hartford?

NCTM Process Standards Analysis and Focus

The standards analysis examines how the process standards have been incorporated into the above lesson. By increasing the focus on three of the process standards, a more effective and meaningful lesson can be presented. The suggestions offered can help you to think about how this might be accomplished.

Representation Student pages show information represented with both single- and double-line graphs, and questions are asked about the information shown.

Suggestion → **Have students examine what information is represented along the axes of the graph and how it is organized. Emphasize the advantages of line graphs and discuss the kinds of information that these graphs best**

Try

Use the table or the graph to answer the questions.

1. Which season has the most precipitation in Portland?
2. In what months do Hartford and Portland have about the same amount of precipitation?

Practice

Joy is thinking about living in Roanoke, Virginia. She made a line graph of temperature data she collected. Since none of the temperatures were below 45°F, she saved space by leaving out this part of the graph. Use the graph she made to answer questions 3–6.

3. What is the warmest month of the year?
4. What is the coldest month of the year?
5. In which months does the average temperature drop below 65°F?
6. If you were planning a vacation, during which months would you visit Roanoke?

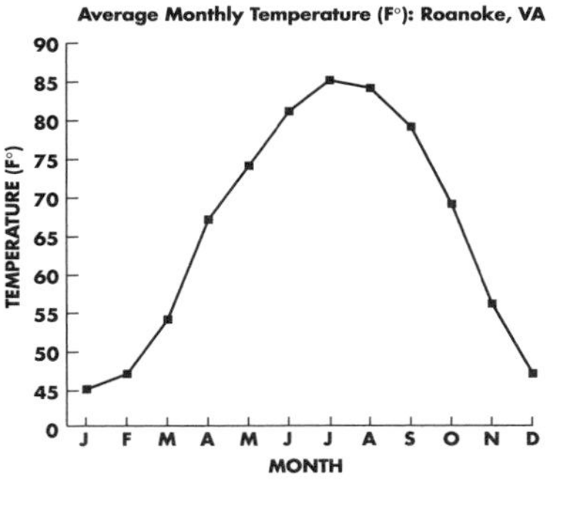

This line graph compares the population growth of two towns. Use the graph to answer the questions.

7. How many more people were living in Blanford than in Feysburg in 1940?
8. How many people were living in Feysburg in 1975?
9. In which decade did Feysburg begin to grow larger than Blanford?

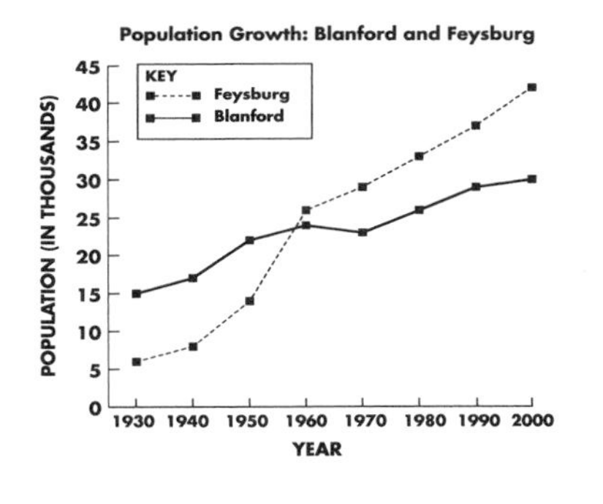

display. Help students determine whether a single- or a double-line graph is appropriate to represent data. Involving students in these activities will help them better understand how to interpret information presented.

Reasoning and Proof The questions in the lesson call for students to interpret data but require minimal reasoning.

Suggestion **→ Encourage students to consider the overall picture presented by the graph and to interpret the information gained from that picture as opposed to concentrating only on specifics. Ask students to think about the reason for graphing the displayed information—who might make such a graph and how the information might be used? This will help students understand how graphs are used to analyze current information and then make predictions about the future.**

Communication The questions presented call for specific information about the graphs and do not invite discussion.

Suggestion **→ Increase the focus on why and how line graphs are created. Communicating their thoughts and insights will make the study of the graphs more meaningful and reinforce students' data analysis skills.**

Problem Solving Interpreting graphs requires reasoning but does not involve problem solving.

Connections Questions are connected to information presented on the graphs. Data are given in the context of real-life situations.

The teaching plan that follows shows how the suggestions for increasing the focus on the process standards can be implemented.

Revised Teaching Plan

f.y.i.

Using an overhead transparency of the graphic information offered here can facilitate the lesson discussion.

Materials → Overhead transparencies of graphs

BEGIN THE LESSON by having students study a table of data and a line graph representing the same data. Use the table and graph shown here, or if you prefer, refer to a single-line graph in your text and adapt questions.

Life Expectancy in the U.S.

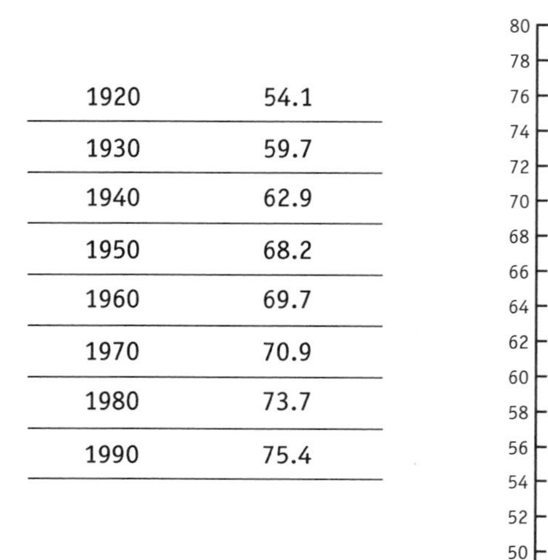

Year	Life Expectancy
1920	54.1
1930	59.7
1940	62.9
1950	68.2
1960	69.7
1970	70.9
1980	73.7
1990	75.4

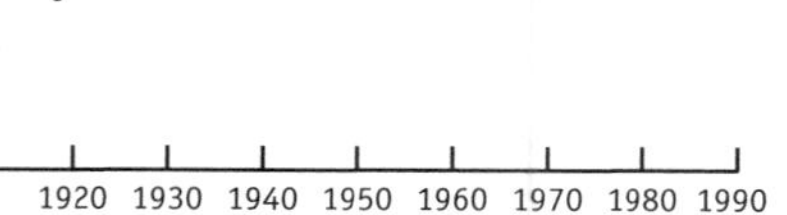

Invite a comparison of the information shown in the table and the graph. Students should be able to articulate that the graph is another way of representing the information in the table. *What are the advantages of displaying this information in a graph?* (The graph gives a quick, overall impression of a lot of numerical data; the graph shows trends over time very clearly.) *What are the advantages of using a table?* (It uses less space, and it is easier to read exact numbers from the table.) *Who might have made a graph of this information? Who would this graph be of interest to? Why?* (Possibilities might include insurance companies to determine rates; architects and builders to consider housing needs; and marketing companies to consider advertising campaigns.)

Continue prompting students to communicate their understanding of the information represented in the graph. *What does the graph represent?* (Life expectancy in U.S.) *What information is presented along the horizontal axis?* (The years being represented) *What size interval is used along the horizontal axis?* (Periods of 10 years) *What information is presented along the vertical axis?* (Average life span in years) *What size interval is used on the vertical axis?* (Two-year intervals) *Why do you think the intervals used were chosen?* (The graph required a reasonable number of intervals to accommodate all the numerical data and make the graph easy to read.) *How do you determine what each data point in the graph represents?* (Each point represents the age of life expectancy for a specific year and can be determined by finding the corresponding intervals along the axes.) *If a point on the graph falls between the intervals, how do you determine what number it represents?* (Estimate the fractional part of the interval, determine what number it represents, and then add this number to the value of the interval just below.)

ENCOURAGE STUDENTS TO INTERPRET the information presented by the graph. *How would you describe the pattern or trend shown by the graph? Does the graph show fluctuation (an up and down pattern), or is there a steady change in one direction (increase or decrease)?* (There is a steady increase, which indicates an *upward trend*.) *During what period did the greatest increase occur?* (From 1920 to 1930 when the increase was 5.6 years.) *Is there a period in which little change occurred?* (Between 1960 and 1970) *How can you determine this by looking at the graph?* (There is a slighter incline of the line.) *What generalizations can you make from looking at this graph?* (Life expectancy in the U.S. has increased steadily during the years from 1920 through 1990.) *How could this graph be used to make some predictions about the future? Why is it useful to be able to make such predictions?* (You might want to make connections to the social, political, and scientific implications of people living longer.)

Point out that the line that connects data points on the graph serves to make reading this information easier, but that intermediate points along the line are not data points and cannot be interpreted as having significant meaning. For example, with the life expectancy graph, we cannot assume that in 1945 the life expectancy was 66 years.

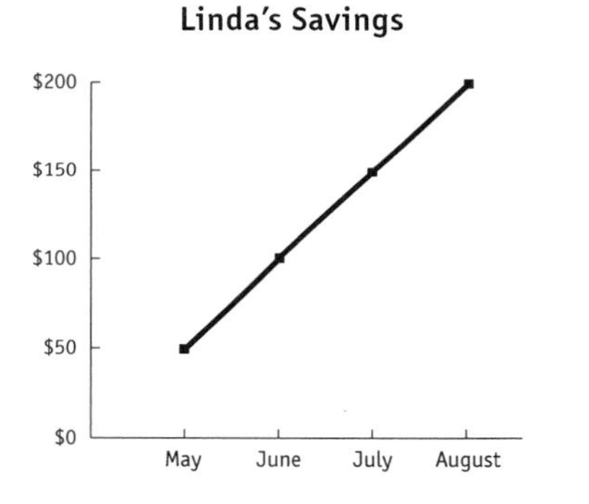

INTRODUCE DOUBLE-LINE GRAPHS and explain that just as double-bar graphs are used to show comparisons, double-line graphs are used to show comparative changes over time. Display a double-line graph, and follow an approach similar to the one used to examine single-line graphs. You may wish to reproduce the graph presented here, which shows weekly totals for two salespeople at an electronics store.

Explain that each line in a double-line graph can be analyzed singly and that the two lines can also be compared. Ask students why a key is necessary. Discuss the types of data that are and are not appropriate for a double-line display. For example, a double-line graph works well to compare the two sales totals over a period of weeks; however this type of graph would not be useful to show the number of televisions and the number of CD players sold by each of four different salespeople. (A double-bar graph would be appropriate for the second case.)

Describe several sets of data and ask students to tell whether they would use a double-line graph to show the information and why. Possible sets might include the average rainfall in two cities over a year, the number of Brand XYX items sold at different locations of the same store over a year, or the number of phone calls received during each day of a week by two different people. Students should be able to determine that double line-graphs would be appropriate to represent the rainfall and the sales because the same type of information is being compared, but that a bar graph would be better for the phone calls.

Finally, have students compare the two graphs of Linda's savings. Point out that each graph shows Linda's savings over a four-month period. What impression does the first graph give? The second graph? What is the same about the graphs and what is different? (Both graphs have the same horizontal scale bar but different vertical scales. Since each vertical interval on the second graph represents only half the amount of money in comparison to the first graph, the rise is greater.) This example will help students recognize the need to examine graphs carefully and think about whether or not they have been used properly.

Conclude the lesson by having students suggest some data sets that could be effectively displayed using a double-line graph. This will reinforce their understanding of what to look for when choosing a graphical display method.

Student Pages

Students are now ready to complete exercises similar to those on the reduced student pages.

Assessment

The questioning approach used in the revised lesson provided many opportunities to assess students' understanding of when to use a single- or double-line graph as well as their ability to read and interpret specific graphs. By noting students' descriptions of general patterns and trends shown in graphs, you could evaluate their ability to analyze and apply visual displays of data.

NCTM Standards Summary

Comparing representations of the same data helped students recognize the advantages of each method and identify what type of information can be effectively displayed in each. Encouraging communication about the purposes and features of single- and double-line graphs reinforced students' understanding of the advantages offered by both. It also helped students to read, interpret, and eventually construct the graphs. Considering the overall picture and identifying patterns or trends enabled students to recognize the value of line graphs as a tool for analyzing information and making predictions. As students explained why two graphs of the same information can give very different visual impressions, they were alerted to the fact that graphs can be misleading, and the need to think critically about how information is represented became clear.

Create Your Own Lesson

THIS LAST CHAPTER IS DESIGNED TO HELP you develop your own lessons in which you can comfortably incorporate the NCTM standards with your teaching style. We start with a list of questions to help you focus on factors to consider as you begin to organize a standards-based lesson. Then, we model the process used to create a lesson as you are walked through the thoughts and decisions one person used in developing a lesson.

The questions listed here are meant as a guide, a starting point; they are offered to get you thinking about how to develop your lesson, what material to cover, what steps to follow, what questions to ask. Hopefully, these questions will trigger additional ideas that you will add as you go along.

Write down the ideas that come to you as you read each question. There may be questions for which you don't have an immediate response, but don't worry; as you begin working on your lesson, ideas will come. Start by selecting the general content area. Think about the concept you want to develop. Then, narrow in on an objective for the lesson. Be specific and be realistic. What does meeting that objective mean? Is there a skill that students should be able to perform after completing the lesson? Are there questions they should be able to answer? How will you determine that the objective has been met?

Next, think about the process standards: Problem Solving, Reasoning and Proof, Communication, Connections, and Representation. What approach will be effective in helping students understand the concept? Try to envision how the lesson will flow, how it should begin, what activities and questions will be included, and how you will assess learning. Understand that there can be several ways to successfully teach any lesson. As you begin to design your lesson, new ideas will come and you will be able to refine your thinking.

Focusing Questions

1. What content standard is to be addressed? What concept within that standard is to be developed?

2. What information do the standards offer about this content?

3. What do students know about this content? What don't they know?

4. What is the specific objective of the lesson? What should students be able to do at the end of the lesson?

recognize	**identify**	**define**
review	**compute**	**classify**
compare	**create**	**other**

5. What kinds of questions should students be able to answer when they complete this lesson? What skill(s) should they be able to demonstrate?

6. What resources are available to develop this concept?

references	**textual material**
manipulatives	**supplementary material**
colleagues	**student knowledge**

7. What can realistically be accomplished in the time allowed?

8. Which activities and process standards can best help develop the key ideas?
   - using drawings, charts, diagrams (Representation)
   - focusing on symbols (Representation)
   - conducting small-group/large-group discussion (Communication)
   - having students gather and analyze data (Problem Solving)
   - thinking through relationships and explaining them (Reasoning and Proof and Communication)
   - finding ways to prove thinking and verify solutions (Reasoning and Proof)
   - extending/building on former knowledge (Connections)
   - integrating the concept with another discipline (Connections)
   - relating math to its use in the real world (Connections)

9. What questions will focus students' thinking on the concept and help guide learning?

Developing the Lesson

I WANT TO DEVELOP A LESSON on the benefits of canceling when multiplying fractions. This is part of the Number and Operation standard. Often students don't cancel before multiplying and so, when they are finished with the multiplication, they often face a difficult task of reducing the product. I want students to understand what canceling does, so they can really see why it is beneficial. My objective for this lesson is to have my students convince themselves to use canceling whenever possible.

Right now some students do not take the time to cancel. I believe that is because they are unsure of what they are doing. They know that if they make a mistake in canceling, they will get an incorrect answer. I want students to try to convince their classmates, one way or the other, that canceling is, or is not, beneficial. Having students do this can generate a good deal of mathematical thinking and reasoning, which the standards emphasize.

Given the importance of representing and communicating ideas, I think this sort of "convince the class" idea lends itself well to such skills. After all, to explain or prove if a method is helpful or not, a student will have to use numbers or symbols or charts, along with spoken words. To be persuasive, he or she will have to develop sound mathematical reasons, represent them in a clear and understandable way, and effectively articulate them. This is a good use of the Representation and Communication process standards.

Now, I'll need to nail down the specifics of the lesson. I think I like the idea of students trying to persuade each other about the benefits or drawbacks of canceling. I believe I can lay out several fraction multiplication problems that involve canceling, and have the students examine them to see if canceling is helpful or not. By solving a problem without canceling, and then solving it again with canceling, they should be able to form an opinion about the strategy.

I will have the students pair together to do the problems, because I think that problem solving, brainstorming ideas, and generating reasons happen best in a group.

The purpose of the first problem I give will be to provide a review of the basic rules of canceling.

Problem 1

Use canceling to solve these problems. Show all your work and be able to tell why you did what you did.

A

$\frac{27}{32} \times \frac{8}{9} = ?$

B

$\frac{5}{8} \times \frac{16}{25} = ?$

Discussing Problem 1

Once all the groups have finished working, I will ask, *Tell me how you canceled.* I want to make sure the students used the proper method, namely divide any numerator and denominator by a common factor. I'll have groups do problems on the board or overhead and walk the class through the steps they used. Some students may mistakenly cancel across both the numerators only and both the denominators only. *Can you cancel across both denominators only, and both numerators only?* What I want to accomplish here, is a short review of why canceling works. Most students can tell me that $\frac{4}{6}$ is the same as $\frac{2}{3}$ because they can divide the numerator and the denominator by 2, which is in effect dividing the fraction by 1, so the value of the fraction does not change although its form does. To help students see why they can cancel across fractions, I will rewrite each problem like this.

$\frac{27 \times 8}{32 \times 9}$

$\frac{5 \times 16}{8 \times 25}$

Here students should be able to see and explain that when they multiply two fractions, they can also think of the fractions broken into different factors. The operation tells them to multiply the numerators and the denominators. They can simplify among factors. In the first problem, students should be able to see that they can divide 27 and 9 by 9. They can divide 32 and 8 by 8. This results in the problem becoming $\frac{3 \times 1}{8 \times 1}$. In the second problem they can see that they can divide 5 and 25 by 5. They can also divide 16 and 8 by 8, resulting in $\frac{1 \times 2}{1 \times 5}$. Once we have reviewed the fundamentals of canceling, we will be ready to go on.

Problem 2

Next, I will give students three more problems. I am giving them explicit instructions. They are to solve each problem twice. The first time, they may not use canceling; the second time, they must. They are to show all their work, then decide whether or not canceling was a helpful thing to do for these problems.

I'll have the students solve the problems both ways—with canceling and without canceling—because I want them to experience the difference as they make an initial decision about whether or not canceling is worth the effort.

C	D	E
$\frac{6}{7} \times \frac{5}{9} \times \frac{14}{15} = ?$	$\frac{15}{16} \times \frac{2}{9} \times \frac{8}{15} = ?$	$\frac{5}{12} \times \frac{3}{10} \times \frac{20}{21} \times \frac{2}{5} = ?$

Discussing Problem 2

I chose the numbers for problems C, D, and E because, without using canceling, the fractional answers can be tricky to reduce. I also wanted to choose problems where canceling was relatively easy to use, and therefore, the problems were easy to solve. The problems allow students to see the difference between the results of canceling versus not canceling. Problem E contains four fractions because I want to show the students that more complex problems—three, four, five fractions to multiply—are easier to solve using canceling.

I will prepare questions that I can use to facilitate a discussion of the problems. *When you didn't cancel, did you run into any difficulties?* I will ask this question because I want the class to see that fractions made from large numbers, like $\frac{364}{546}$, are difficult to reduce, and that it's easy to make reducing errors with fractions made from large numbers. To emphasize this point, I will ask, *Would you rather reduce the fractions $\frac{364}{546}$ or have the answer in lowest terms?* In terms of a problem like problem C, I expect some students to multiply across the numerators and denominators correctly, arriving at $\frac{364}{546}$, but eventually wind up with the wrong answer because of errors made while reducing. I want the class to see that canceling correctly can get them to an answer that contains fractions in the lowest possible terms. The answer to problem C is $\frac{4}{9}$, D is $\frac{1}{9}$, E is $\frac{1}{21}$.

I'll next ask the class to focus on their use of canceling in these problems. *Did canceling help you solve these problems?* I'll ask this so the students can start thinking about the benefits of canceling. Multiplying without canceling in problem D leads to $\frac{240}{2160}$ needing to be reduced. By canceling ahead of time, the fraction is quickly boiled down to $\frac{1}{9}$. If students have solved the problem correctly both ways, the benefits of canceling should be evident.

Problem 3

Plan a brief presentation to your classmates to convince them that they should, or should not, use canceling. You must show sample problems to support your arguments.

Discussing Problem 3

Pairs of students will take turns presenting to the class. After each group presents, I will ask students to question the presenters. I will use the following questions. *Were the presenters convincing? Why or why not?* I'll ask this because I want the presenters and the class to focus on the basis of the persuasive argument. *Did the presenters back up their arguments with clear examples? Did they show different fraction problems, and compute them correctly, to show their opinion of canceling? Or was there little mathematical basis for their arguments?* Presenters who make statements like "You should use canceling because it works better" will be challenged. *Can you give an example with some fractions?* I want the class to consider both methods—canceling versus not canceling—so they can see for themselves the benefits of canceling.

I am hoping that there are a few groups who oppose using canceling. I want a debate to ensue, because by arguing their points of view and being rigorously challenged by an opponent, the students will really have to come up with sound mathematical reasons to support their opinions. Also, students need to understand that there are opportunities to make mistakes while canceling. I will want to prepare some problems to challenge both groups with, some where canceling helps and some where canceling is not possible.

Reviewing the Plan

Before I actually teach this lesson, I'll write it up and review it again to make sure it meets my goals and uses the standards effectively. Overall, I feel good about it. I think my sixth graders will enjoy the persuasion aspect of the lesson. The problems give the students a chance to really see how canceling is a handy tool to keep in their mathematical toolboxes. And, the presenting of ideas goes a long way toward having students communicate their mathematical thinking, as well as use different ways of representing mathematical methods. Finally, I believe the students will get an effective dose of reasoning and proof when they try to convince the class about canceling.